# TREASURES
*from*
# FRED PENNER'S PLACE

**Treasures from Fred Penner's Place**

Based on the Canadian Broadcasting Corporation
Children's Television Series, "Fred Penner's Place."

© Copyright 1992 by Pat Patterson and Peg McKelvey

Fitzhenry & Whiteside Limited
91 Granton Drive
Richmond Hill, Ontario L4B 2N5

Production by Peg McKelvey
Typesetting by ISIS Communications Limited
Piano arrangements by Jack Turner
Music Typesetting by David Nichol Music Printing
Cover design by Word & Image
Cover photo and photo on page 6
   by Garry Kopelow, courtesy CBC
Other photography by Montizambert, Vancouver, B.C.

Printed and bound in Hong Kong
   by Wing King Tong Co. Ltd.

**Canadian Cataloguing in Publication Data**

Main entry under title:

Treasures from Fred Penner's place

Includes index.
ISBN 1-55041-039-3 (bound) ISBN 1-55041-063-6 (pbk.)

1. Children's songs. 2. Children's stories,
English. 3. Children's poetry, English.
I. Patterson, Pat. II. McKelvey, Peg. III. Day,
Marie. IV. Title: Fred Penner's Place (Television
program).

M1990.T74 1991     782.42'083     C91-094281-1

# TREASURES
## *from*
# FRED PENNER'S PLACE

Edited by
Pat Patterson and Peg McKelvey

Illustrations by Marie Day

Based on the Canadian Broadcasting Corporation
Children's Television Series, *Fred Penner's Place*

**Fitzhenry & Whiteside**

# Contents

**Songs**

# Contents

**Stories, Poems and Rhymes**

You can visit "Fred Penner's Place" by way of your television set. Fred gets here each day through this hollow log in a secret part of the forest. A few of Fred's grownup friends know how to find the hollow log too, and they are all people who like to sing, so Fred sometimes invites one of these friends to come and sing along with him. You, of course, can sing along with Fred all the time if you like. And you can learn lots of the songs he sings, because they're right here in this book.

Dozens of the stories that Fred has told are here too — some very old stories told in a new way, and some new stories written especially for Fred. You'll also find pictures of other regular visitors — Renée Raccoon, Dilly Duck and the Wordbird — along with some poems, riddles and jokes that are just for fun.

# THE MORE WE ARE TOGETHER

Traditional

The more we are to - geth - er, to - geth - er, to - geth - er, The

more we are to - geth - er, the hap - pi - er we'll be. For

your friends are my friends, and my friends are your friends. The

more we are to - geth - er, the hap - pi - er we'll be.

# FRIENDS

Words and Music by
Bob King

1. A sha-dow's al-ways there when the sun shines. A turn is al-ways there when the

road winds. Dogs are al-ways there when you feed them. Friends are al-ways there when you

need them. Friends are friends and friends are fine. Friends are friends and

you are mine. Friends are friends I hear them say.

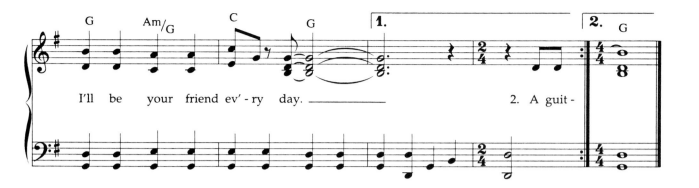

I'll be your friend ev'-ry day. _____

2. A guit-

2. A guitar is always there when you play it.
A poem is always there when you say it.
Books are always there when you read them.
Friends are always there when you need them.
Friends are friends and friends are fine.
Friends are friends and you are mine.
Friends are friends I hear them say.
I'll be your friend ev'ry day.

**Finger Play**

A little boy lived in this house.   (*Make fist with right hand, thumb hidden.*)
A little girl lived in this house.   (*Make fist with left hand, thumb hidden.*)
The little boy came out of his house.   (*Release right thumb.*)
And the little girl came out of her house.   (*Release left thumb.*)
They both looked up and down the street.   (*Move both thumbs slowly.*)
They saw each other.   (*Point thumbs toward each other.*)
They walked across the street and shook hands.   (*Move thumbs until they meet.*)
And they promised to play together in the afternoon.   (*Wiggle thumbs.*)
Then the little boy went back into his house.   (*Tuck right thumb into fist.*)
And the little girl went back into her house.   (*Tuck left thumb into fist.*)

*Talking with your hands is called "signing."*
*Try these three signs that say "I like you."*

"I"

"Like"

"You"

## I LIKE YOU

Words and Music by
Terry McManus

1. I like you. Flow-ers like rain, I like you. I'll say it a - gain, I like you.
2. Sun comes up, sun goes down, This big world goes round and round, We can talk with-

# The Lonely Little Skunk

*by Peg McKelvey*

Once upon a time there was a baby skunk called Rosie, who lived with her family in the forest. She had a mother and two brothers and a sister, and their home was a lovely little cave hollowed out beneath the roots of a big tree.

One day, there was a very bad storm. The rain poured, the thunder roared, and a bolt of lightning hit the big tree and knocked it over. The cave filled up with water, and all the skunks except Rosie were swept away by the flood.

Rosie held on tight to a root of the tree, and by the next day the water had drained away. But there was no sign of her mother and her little brothers and sister. Rosie was all alone.

Rosie set off to see if she could find her family. The first animal she met was a rabbit.

Rosie ran up to him and said, "Mister Rabbit, have you seen my mother and my brothers and my sister?"

Well, Randy Rabbit took one sniff at Rosie and said, "Phee-ew!" And then he ran away as fast as he could.

Poor lonely Rosie went on through the forest until she saw a big black bear.

Rosie ran up to her and said, "Mrs. Bear, have you seen my mother and my brothers and my sister?"

Well, Bertha Bear took one sniff at Rosie and said, "Phee-ew!" And then she lumbered off as fast as she could.

Poor lonely Rosie went on through the forest until she saw a huge moose.

Rosie ran up to him and said, "Mister Moose, have you seen my mother and my brothers and my sister?"

Well, Morris Moose pawed the ground and roared, "Phee-ew!" And he galloped away as fast as he could.

Poor little Rosie sat down and cried. "Why," she said to herself, "why do all these big strong animals run away from me? And what do they mean by that funny word 'phee-ew'?" You see, Rosie didn't know that skunks have a special smell all of their own that only other skunks love.

While Rosie sat there, a little breeze came up and blew through the woods. Rosie put her nose in the air and sniffed. Ohhhh — there was the most delicious smell!

So Rosie set off once again, and she followed that lovely smell through the woods, and across the meadow, and up the hill. Rosie looked all around from the top of the hill, and can you guess what she saw?

Down at the bottom of the hill, Rosie saw her mother, and her two brothers, and her sister — all safe and sound! And when Rosie ran to them to say hello, everybody hugged her and sniffed her, and *nobody* said "Phee-ew!"

*Here's a tongue-twister from the Wordbird:*
A skunk sat on a stump.
The skunk stunk
But the skunk thunk the stump stunk.

# Fat Cat

*by Janis Nostbakken*

Once upon a time there was a cat — a fluffy, furry, fat cat, who loved to spend her days snoozing in the sun. On sunny days she would settle herself on her favourite mat under the window and soak up the sun's warm rays.

One day, as the fat cat sat on the mat, she spied with her little eye what she thought at first was a mouse. But she soon realized that it was a rat — a fat rat! So the fat cat chased the fat rat all around the house.

Round and round they went until the fat rat found a hiding spot right under a hat! There sat the fat rat under the hat, while the fat cat searched this way and that.

"Drat!" said the fat cat. "Where can that fat rat be at?" Just then, she saw the hat move. "Aha!" she said to herself. "That rat is under the hat!"

With one pounce, the cat sat on that hat until it was almost flat. Alas and alack, that's when the lady of the house came back. She gave the fat cat a pat, and then noticed her hat. It was flat! Drat!

"Scat, brat!" she cried, and the fat cat ran. So did the fat rat, and so did the lady. She picked up a baseball bat and chased that fat rat right out of the house.

Then she gave the fat cat another pat, and they had a little chat as the cat sat down on her mat to sleep in the sun once more.

Now what do you think of that?

## Hey Diddle Diddle

Hey diddle diddle, the cat and the fiddle,
The cow jumped over the moon;
The little dog laughed to see such sport,
And the dish ran away with the spoon!

## I Love Little Pussy

I love little pussy,
Her coat is so warm;
And if I don't hurt her,
She'll do me no harm.

I'll not pull her tail,
Nor drive her away,
But pussy and I
Together will play.

She will sit by my side
And I'll give her some food,
And pussy will love me
Because I am good.

## Pussy Cat, Pussy Cat

Pussy cat, pussy cat, where have you been?
I've been to London to visit the Queen.
Pussy cat, pussy cat, what did you there?
I frightened a little mouse under her chair.

# THE CAT CAME BACK

Harry S. Miller
Adapted by Fred Penner

1. Now old Mis-ter John-son had troub-les of his own; He had a yel-low cat who

would-n't leave his home. He tried and he tried to give the cat a-way; He

gave it to a man go-ing far, far, a-way. _____ But the

cat came back the ve-ry next day. The cat came back; they

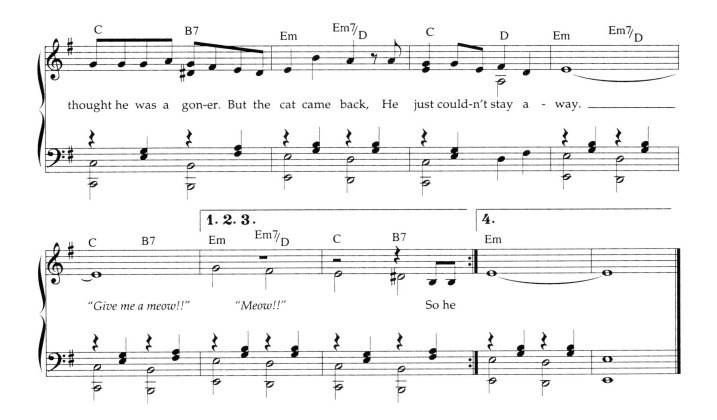

thought he was a gon-er. But the cat came back, He just could-n't stay a - way. _____

**1. 2. 3.** "Give me a meow!!" "Meow!!"

**4.** So he

2. So he gave it to a man going up in a balloon;
   He told him for to take it to the man in the moon.
   The balloon came down about ninety miles away;
   Where the man is now, well, I dare not say.
   *Chorus:* But the cat came back, etc.

3. So he gave it to a man going 'way out west;
   He told him for to take it to the one he loved the best.
   First the train hit the track, then it jumped a rail;
   Not a soul was left behind to tell the gruesome tale.
   *Chorus:* But the cat came back, etc.

4. Then he put it in a rocket ship bound for Mars;
   For seven days and seven nights it flew to the stars.
   It crashed against an asteroid in the middle of space;
   Pieces floated everywhere and left no trace.
   *Chorus:* But the cat came back, etc.

# The Lion and the Mouse

*Based on a fable by Aesop*

One day, after hours of hunting, a great lion found himself feeling weak from the heat of the blazing sun, and tired from the long way he had travelled, so he lay down on a grassy spot shaded by a tree. Soon he fell fast asleep and began to snore.

A little while later, a tiny mouse who didn't know where he was going ran right over the lion's nose. His little feet tickled and wakened the lion, who sat up with a huge sneeze.

"Achoo! Who ran over my nose? Who was it now? Speak up!" And he caught sight of the little mouse, who was shaking with fright. "I've got you!" the lion roared, as he clapped a great paw over the tiny mouse. "I shall eat you up in one bite!"

"Oh, please, Mister Lion," pleaded the mouse. "I didn't mean to run over your honourable nose. I just lost my way. Please don't harm me. Why, to one as great and brave as you, surely a tiny mouse like me is not worth bothering about!"

The lion thought about that. Then he grumbled, "Oh, all right. I'll let you go this once, but stay clear of my nose next time! For that matter, you'd better say clear of all lions!"

"Oh, I will sir," said the mouse, "I certainly will. Thank you, sir." And he ran away, happy and grateful to be free.

It was only a few days later, when the lion was walking through the woods, that he came to a place where some hunters had set a trap, and before he knew what was happening, he fell into a huge hole and became so entangled in ropes that he couldn't move, no matter how hard he struggled. The lion roared in pain and anger. "Help! Help!" he cried. "Help me, please!"

Not far away, a tiny creature heard the lion's voice. It was the little mouse that the lion had set free, and he ran through the forest as fast as he could, until he came to the trap where the lion lay.

The mouse started work right away, chewing the ropes that held the big lion. He chewed and chewed and chewed some more, and after a time, when the lion gave a mighty tug, the chewed rope broke and the lion was free! He gently picked up the little mouse and held him softly in his paw. "Thank you, mouse, thank you," he said. "I shall always be grateful for your kindness."

"My pleasure!" squeaked the mouse. "It was the least I could do for a friend."

# I WISH I WAS

Traditional

3. I wish I was a squirrel with a big long tail.
   Wish I was a squirrel with a big long tail.
   If I was a squirrel with a big long tail
   I'd spread it out and away I'd sail.
   I wish I was a squirrel with a big long tail.

4. I wish I was a fuzzy wuzzy fox.
   Wish I was a fuzzy wuzzy fox.
   If I was a fuzzy wuzzy fox
   I wouldn't have to change my socks.
   I wish I was a fuzzy wuzzy fox.

*There is also a poem called "I Wish I Was."*
*You can sing it to the tune of "The Farmer in the Dell."*

### I Wish I Was

I wish I was some mud,
I wish I was some mud,
I'd ooze and ooze in somebody's shoes,
I wish I was some mud.

*Here's a verse that Fred made up . . .*

I wish I was a cow,
I wish I was a cow,
I'd moo and moo till the milk turned blue,
I wish I was a cow.

### Star Wish

Star light, star bright,
First star I see tonight,
I wish I may, I wish I might,
Have the wish I wish tonight.

# The Three Wishes

*A modern version of an old fairy tale*

Sometimes, you have to be just a little bit careful when you make a wish. This story will tell you why.

Once upon a time, not so long ago, there was a poor fisherman called Jack, who lived in a little house beside the sea.

One day Jack caught a beautiful silver fish on his line, and he was just about to take it off the hook when the fish said, "Oh please, Jack, put me back in the water."

What's this? A talking fish?

The fish then said, "If you will put me back in the water, I will give you and your wife three wishes."

Three wishes!

Jack said to the fish, "If I wish for, one, a brand new house . . . and two, a new car . . . and three, a million dollars — will you grant all my wishes?"

"Whatever you wish will come true," said the fish.

"Swim away home, friend," said Jack. And he threw the beautiful silver fish back into the water. Then he ran all the way back to his little house to tell his wife about their good fortune.

But when he got there, his wife was not home.

By this time, Jack was very hungry, and he said to himself, "I wish I had a nice big peanut butter sandwich with lettuce and strawberry jam."

Guess what? Jack got his wish! Instead of a brand new house, he had a peanut butter sandwich with lettuce and strawberry jam.

Just then, Jack's wife came home, and Jack told her the whole story.

Jack's wife was very angry. "Do you mean to say we could have had a brand new house and all you got was a peanut butter sandwich with lettuce and strawberry jam? What a fool you are, Jack. I wish that peanut butter sandwich was stuck to your ear."

As soon as Jack's wife said that, the peanut butter sandwich jumped up and stuck to Jack's ear. Jack and his wife pulled and yanked, and yanked and pulled, but that peanut butter sandwich would not come unstuck.

At last Jack knew what he had to do. "I wish this sandwich would come unstuck!" he yelled.

And it did.

Poor Jack. He didn't get a brand new house. He didn't get a new car. He didn't get a million dollars. All he got was a peanut butter sandwich with lettuce and strawberry jam!

# SING US ANOTHER ONE, DO

Traditional

*Verse*

There once was a man who was weird _____ He said "It is just as I feared. _____ Two

owls and a hen   Four larks and a wren  Have all built their nests in my   beard." _____

*Chorus*

That   was a   cute lit-tle song. . Sing us an-oth-er one do. _____ 2. There   do. _____

2. There once was a fellow named Jack
   Who smiled when he sat on a tack.
   Said he, "I am feeling
   I might hit the ceiling.
   I hope that it doesn't hit back!"

3. There was a young lady named Wright
   Who travelled much faster than light.
   She set out one day
   In a relative way,
   And arrived on the previous night.

4. There once was a man from Peru
   Who dreamed he was eating his shoe.
   When he woke in a fright
   In the dark of the night,
   He found it was perfectly true.

5. A tutor who tooted the flute
   Tried to tutor two tooters to toot.
   Said the two to the tutor,
   "Is it tougher to toot, or
   To tutor two tooters to toot?"

6. A man who was dining at Crewe
   Found quite a large mouse in his stew.
   Said the waiter, "Don't shout
   And wave it about,
   Or the rest will be wanting one too!"

7. There was an old man from Calcutta
   Who coated his tonsils with butter.
   It converted his snore
   From a thunderous roar
   To a soft and melodious mutter.

# The North Wind and the Sun

*Based on a fable by Aesop*

Once upon a time, the North Wind shouted to the Sun, "I'm stronger than you are; that's for sure!"

The Sun, shining brightly, replied, "Nonsense, my friend! There never was a wind as strong as the Sun!"

They argued back and forth until it became quite silly. "I am." "You're not." "I am." "You're not." You know how quarrels like that can go on.

After a time, the Sun and the North Wind decided they would test their strength, to see who was right. "Look," said the North Wind. "That man walking there — the one with the heavy coat. I bet I can get that coat off him before you can."

"Go ahead. Try," said the Sun, and the Wind began to blow with all his strength. His icy cold blast nearly blew the man off his feet, but the harder the Wind blew, the more tightly the man wrapped his coat around him, to protect himself from the Wind and the cold.

Before long, the North Wind was exhausted. He had hardly a breath left, but he had not been able to get the man's coat off. "*You* won't be able to do it either," he said to the Sun. "Nobody is stronger than I am!"

The Sun smiled, and sent his warm beams towards the ground, making the cold fog disappear, and sending great waves of warmth towards the man in the heavy coat. In a little while, the man took off his woollen muffler. Soon after that, he removed his hat and his gloves. "That's nothing!" snarled the North Wind. "His coat! Make him take off his coat!"

"Certainly," said the Sun, turning brighter and brighter, until the man below was so hot that he took off his coat, put it in his pack, mopped his forehead and rolled up his shirt sleeves! "Well?" said the Sun.

"You win," whispered the North Wind. He was so tired from all that blowing that a whisper was all he could manage.

The Sun just went on smiling.

## The North Wind Doth Blow

The north wind doth blow,
And we shall have snow,
And what will poor Robin do then, poor thing?

He'll sit in a barn,
And keep himself warm,
And hide his head under his wing, poor thing.

# I AM THE WIND

Words and Music by
Fred Penner

*Chorus:* I am the wind, etc.

2. I can make music that's gentle and sweet,
   Whistles and chimes that you hear
   In the streets of the city or down country roads,
   In the day or the night I am near.
   *Chorus:* I am the wind, etc.

3. I love to play every day of the year,
   Helping seasons to come and to go.
   The flowers and plants wait for me in the spring
   To carry seeds to places they grow.
   *Chorus:* I am the wind, etc.

# Billy Baloo's Balloon

*by Pat Patterson*

In the small town where Billy Baloo lived, there was a wonderful fall fair in October every year.

The fair had stands where people sold homemade cakes and jams. There were games that brought the winners big pink teddy bears for prizes. There were contests to choose the prettiest baby, the fattest pig and the cleverest mongrel dog. There was a merry-go-round, a tall ferris wheel and a ride called the Twirlygig. But for Billy Baloo, one thing was more exciting than anything else at the fair. It was a balloon — a huge passenger balloon with a basket which carried people for rides away up in the air. While it was anchored to the ground, the pilot stood beside it, shouting, "This way, ladies and gents! Get your tickets for the wonderful balloon ride. See the world from up in the sky! The thrill of a lifetime for only five dollars!"

Billy Baloo certainly didn't have five dollars and besides, his father had been very firm on this subject. "Don't get any ideas about going up in that balloon, young man," he said. "It's far too dangerous!"

Every day, Billy stood and watched as people climbed into the balloon's basket, the ropes were cast off, and up, up they went, to sail away on the wind. And every day he'd be there when the pilot did whatever he did to bring the balloon safely back to earth, exactly where it had started from.

Having seen Billy standing there day after day, with a look of longing on his face, the balloon pilot felt sorry for him. "Tell you what, son," he said, "while the balloon is tied down to the ground, you can stand in its basket for a while and *pretend* to be flying. How's that?"

Billy thanked the pilot and happily climbed into the balloon's basket. He was pretending he was up in the air, and the pilot was busy selling tickets when something almost unbelievable happened. The knot in the rope which held the balloon to the ground suddenly

slipped. There was a jerk as a gust of wind caught the balloon, and
Billy nearly lost his balance. He grabbed the edge of the basket to
steady himself, just as the rope slipped from its anchor completely,
and the balloon sailed up, up, up into the sky.

Billy Baloo was both thrilled and frightened. He looked down and
saw the pilot waving his arms frantically, and all the people in the fairground staring up at the balloon. To Billy they looked as small as ants
and the merry-go-round looked no bigger than a cookie. Suddenly, the
balloon was swept sideways by a strong breeze, and Billy saw the
fairground disappear. "I'm alone!" he thought. "Just me — and the
balloon."

31

He certainly was alone and, for now, the balloon was his very own. It was Billy Baloo's balloon. Billy decided to enjoy the flight as much as he could. Looking down, he saw cars and buses which seemed like little toys, and houses as tiny as sugar cubes. He passed over shining lakes and a forest where the trees were thick and green.

When he flew over the forest for the second time, Billy realized that the wind had changed direction. The balloon was being blown back towards the fairground. "Hooray!" he shouted. Then he remembered that being blown back was one thing and getting down to earth was another.

A huge bird flew around the balloon, and Billy called, "Oh, bird, what am I to do?" He didn't expect an answer, of course, and wasn't surprised when the bird disappeared. Now the fairground came in sight, and there he was, still in the air.

A moment later, Billy's heart nearly stopped with excitement. He felt the balloon dip down slightly. Perhaps he imagined it, but no. Slowly and steadily, the balloon began to float towards the earth. But why?

What Billy didn't know was that the huge bird he had seen was perched on the very top of the balloon. It had taken a good sharp peck at it, to find out what kind of a thing this was. The bird's beak had made a hole, and the light gas which kept the balloon up in the air was gradually escaping through the hole!

Billy watched, limp with relief, as the ground came closer and closer. The crowd of people was still there, larger than ever, with fire engines and ambulances and hordes of police in cars and on horses, all expecting something terrible to happen.

Instead, the balloon simply floated down and landed with hardly a bump and everyone burst into cheers and applause. "Hooray for Billy Baloo!" they shouted, as Billy's grateful father picked him up out of the basket.

The pilot was so happy to see Billy and the balloon safely back that he decided to give his balloon a name. From then on, it was known everywhere as "The Billy Baloo Balloon."

## Simple Simon

Simple Simon met a pieman
Going to the fair.
Said Simple Simon to the pieman,
"Let me taste your ware."

Said the pieman to Simple Simon,
"Show me first your penny."
Said Simple Simon to the pieman,
"Indeed I have not any."

Simple Simon went a-fishing
For to catch a whale;
All the water he had got
Was in his mother's pail.

Simple Simon went to look
If plums grew on a thistle;
He pricked his fingers very much
Which made poor Simon whistle.

Fred's feathered friend is the Wordbird, who is a very important fellow around "Fred Penner's Place." He even has his own song, which you'll find on page 98.

When the Wordbird comes to perch on his favourite tree, he usually has a piece of paper in his beak, and on the paper is the word of the day. You can learn what the word means and how to spell it, with a little help from Fred and the Wordbird.

In this picture the word of the day is "shoe" and you'll want to wear shoes for the song on the next page.

# WALKING

Words and Music by
Mark Baldwin

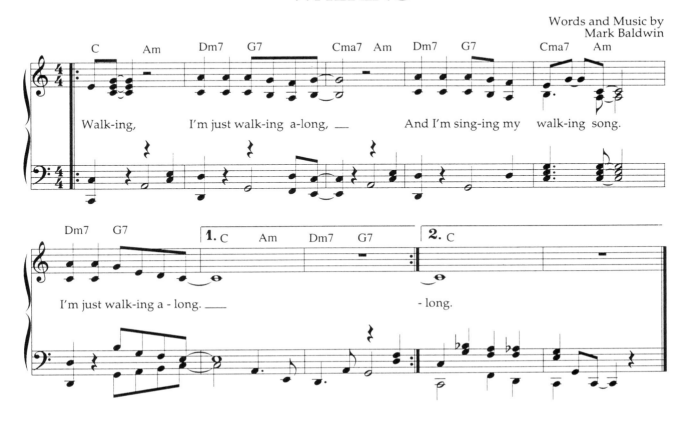

Walk-ing, I'm just walk-ing a-long, ___ And I'm sing-ing my walk-ing song.

I'm just walk-ing a - long. ___ - long.

# Gail the Snail

*by Janis Nostbakken*

Once upon a time, in a lovely little garden, there lived a snail named Gail. She spent most of her time creeping along ever so slowly looking for leaves to eat. Wherever she went, her house went with her, for her house was the shell she carried on her back.

One misty morning, Gail Snail was busily nibbling a bit of leaf when a toad came hop-hop-hopping through the flower bed. "Good morning! I'm Rhoda — Rhoda Toad. Won't you come hopping through the garden with me?"

Gail Snail was surprised. "Oh, I'd love to," she said, "but I'm afraid I can't hop anywhere with this house on my back."

"Pity," said Rhoda Toad. "Hopping is the only way to get around." And with that, she hopped off singing her hopping song:

"Hopping, I'm just hopping along,
 And I'm singing my hopping song.
 I'm just hopping along."

No sooner had the toad left than a duck came widdley-waddling up from the pond. "Good morning! I'm Chuck — Chuck Duck. Won't you come waddling through the garden with me?"

"I'd love to," said Gail Snail, "but I can't waddle anywhere with this house on my back."

"Too bad," said Chuck Duck. "Waddling is the only way to get around." And with that, he waddled off singing his waddling song:

"Waddling, I'm just waddling along,
 And I'm singing my waddling song.
 I'm just waddling along."

No sooner had the duck left than a squirrel came running into the garden. "Good morning! I'm Pearl — Pearl Squirrel. Won't you come running through the garden with me?"

"Oh, I'd love to," said Gail Snail, "but I can't run anywhere with this house on my back."

"Tut-tut," said Pearl Squirrel. "Running is the only way to get around." And with that, the squirrel ran off singing her running song:

> "Running, I'm just running along,
>  And I'm singing my running song.
>  I'm just running along."

By this time, Gail Snail was beginning to feel sorry for herself. She couldn't hop like Rhoda Toad. She couldn't waddle like Chuck Duck, and she certainly couldn't run like Pearl Squirrel. All she could do was quietly creep about. If only she didn't have to carry her heavy house wherever she went, perhaps then she could hop or waddle or run.

Just then, a hungry crow named Joe came swooping out of the sky. He was looking for breakfast, and a juicy snail would do very nicely.

"Eeek!" cried Gail. And she quickly pulled herself inside her shell house to hide. There she sat waiting and waiting and waiting, until at last it was safe for her to come out again.

"Phew! That was close!" thought Gail. "My house may be too heavy for me to hop or waddle or run, but it's the best hiding place in the garden!" And with that, Gail Snail crept off singing her creeping song:

> "Creeping, I'm just creeping along,
>  And I'm singing my creeping song.
>  I'm just creeping along."

# SAILING ACROSS THE SEA

Music: Traditional
Words by Peg McKelvey and Pat Patterson

1. Haul up the sail, there's a breeze on the bay, Blow-ing for
2. High ov-er-head a wa-ter bird glides free as the

you and me, _____ West-er-ly wind come and
air is free _____ O - ver the waves our

take us a - way, Sail - ing a - cross the sea. _____
lit - tle boat rides Sail - ing a - cross the sea. _____

Clouds in the sky hur-ry on by, Por - pois-es jump for
We'll sing a song cruis-ing a - long, Un - der the set - ting

# Bert Meets a Bear

*by Peg McKelvey*

You can help to tell this story by making the sounds. Let's practise a bit before we begin.

You can make the sound of a horse walking by slapping your knees: 1-2, 1-2, 1-2.

Now the horse is going to trot. It's almost the same sound as walking, only faster: **1**-2, **1**-2, **1**-2.

When the horse gallops, its feet make a different rhythm: 1-2-3, 1-2-3, 1-2-3.

Have you ever heard a horse whinny? Try it! (*Whinny!*)

Have you ever heard a coyote howl? Try that one too. (*Howl!*)

What do you think a bear sounds like? Like this? (*Roar!*)

In this story, Bert has to walk through a swamp. It sounds like this. (*Slurp, slurp, slurp!*) Can you do that?

Can you make a sound like a gate with a rusty hinge? (*Squeeeeeeak!*)

Now you're ready to help tell the story.

Once in an earlier time there was a man called Bert who lived on a ranch out west, near the mountains.

Bert knew about a cave in the mountains, and he had heard that there was treasure up there. So one day he decided to saddle up his horse Misty and go and look for the treasure.

Bert went out to the corral and called, "Misty! Come on, girl!"

Here she comes! (*Gallop. Whinny!*)

Bert got up on Misty and they rode out of the corral. (*Walk.*) Bert closed the gate behind them. (*Squeak!*) Misty trotted across the prairie at an easy pace. (*Trot.*)

Away off in the distance they heard a coyote. (*Howl!*)

It was coming closer! (*Louder howl!*)

Bert said, "Giddy-up, Misty. Let's go! Yahooo!" (*Gallop.*)

Misty galloped as hard as she could (*Gallop*) and they got away from that coyote. (*Distant howl!*)

After a while, they came to a swamp, and Misty refused to go any further. (*Loud whinny.*)

Bert tried to persuade her to go on. "Come on, old girl," said Bert. But Misty would not go into that swamp. (*Whinny.*)

"Aw, Misty, please?" said Bert.

But Misty would not go. (*Whinny.*)

So Bert got off Misty, and tied her to a tree. Then he started to walk through the swamp. (*Slurp, slurp, slurp.*) It was very slow going. (*Slurp, slurp, slurp.*)

At last Bert got to the other side of the swamp and started to climb up the mountain.

Bert climbed (*Puff, puff*) and climbed (*Puff, puff*) and climbed (*Puff, puff*) till he came to the mouth of the big cave.

(*Whisper.*) Bert went into the cave very quietly. It was dark.

Suddenly, there was a roar! (*Roar!*) The cave was the home of a big black bear!

Bert turned around and ran down the mountain. (*Puff, puff, puff!*) He ran across the swamp. (*Slurp, slurp, slurp!*) He jumped on Misty's back and they galloped across the prairie. (*Whinny! Gallop.*)

At last they came to their own corral. (*Loud whinny!*) Bert opened the gate (*Squeak!*) and closed it behind them. (*Squeak!*)

They were safe at home. For the rest of his life, Bert stayed a long way away from that cave.

# The Talkative Turtle

*Based on an English folk tale*

The talkative turtle lived in the soft mud beside a pool, dozing away the hours. But when he woke up, he would not stop talking.

"Good morning, good morning, good morning, world. Good gracious me! If I hadn't woken up this very minute I would still be fast asleep. Fast asleep, that is, if I hadn't woken up. And if I hadn't woken up, I might have slept all day. I suppose I must have slept enough, or I wouldn't have woken up . . ."

The turtle talked on and on. Of course, he never listened to anyone else. He talked so much that he ended up talking to himself.

One day, when he was busy talking to himself, two ducks flew down to drink at the turtle's pool.

"Well, hello, hello, hello, hello, ducks," said the turtle. "I've just been thinking. It must be great, just great, to be able to fly, high up, like you do, looking down at the world, the wind whistling through your wings, the sky blue above you. Will you take me flying with you?"

"Whoever heard of a turtle flying?" said one of the ducks. "Turtles have no wings."

But the other duck saw a stick poking up out of the mud and that gave her an idea.

"We could carry him between us," she said. We could hold the stick in our beaks, and the turtle can hang on with his mouth."

"Oh yes," said the turtle, "what a marvellous idea, just marvellous. I'll hang on tight and we can go flying, high up, looking down at the world, the wind whistling through my . . . through my shell, the sky blue above me . . ."

One of the ducks interrupted him. "You won't be able to talk, Turtle, or you'll fall off the stick."

"Of course I won't talk," said the turtle. "Nothing, nothing, nothing at all can possibly make me talk."

So the turtle took hold of the middle of the stick with his mouth.
The ducks spread their wings, and lifted the stick into the air. They
flew high over the pool, with the turtle dangling between them. He
hung on and didn't say a word as they flew up and up, over the hills
and over the towns.

Some boys and girls saw them flying by. "Look, look,
everybody!" they shouted. "Come and see! Two ducks carrying a
turtle!" Who had ever seen such a sight before? They pointed and
giggled and laughed.

This made the turtle *furious*. He worked himself up into a rage.
"Rrrrrrr!" He knew just what to say to them!

And the turtle opened his mouth and shouted, "Silly children!"

Down, down, down he fell. Down, down, down — phlump!

The ducks flew back to see if the turtle was all right. It had been
a long way down.

But they needn't have worried. There was the turtle, unhurt,
sitting where he had landed in the soft mud by the pool. He was
telling another turtle about his adventure. She wasn't much of a talker,
but she loved to listen.

So the talkative turtle went on talking, and talking, and talking,
on and on. He told everybody who would listen about that wonderful
day when he went flying with two ducks.

Learning to sing this song in French is quite easy. The words ask "Can you play the violin? The flute? The drum?" The answer imitates the sound of the instrument.

"Bonhomme" means "good man" or "good fellow." Bonhomme is also the name of the jovial talking snowman who is the symbol of the Winter Carnival held every year in Quebec City.

## BONHOMME! (GOOD MAN!)

Traditional

1. Bon-homm', Bon-homm', sais-tu jou - er? Bon-homm', Bon-homm', sais-tu jou - er? sais - tu jou-

*Repeat for each new instrument you sing.*

- er de ce vio - lon - la? Sais - tu jou - er de ce vio - lon - la? Zing, zing, zing de ce vio - lon-

- la? Zing, zing, zing de ce vio - lon - la? Bon - homm', _____ Tu n'est pas maitr' dans ta mai-

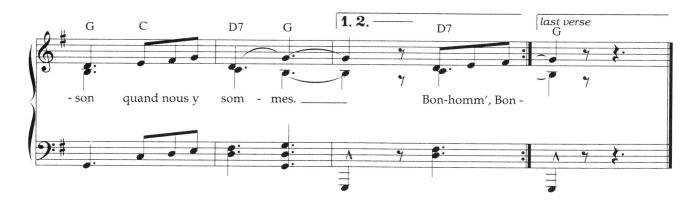

- son    quand nous y    som - mes. _____    Bon-homm', Bon -

2. Bonhomm', Bonhomm', sais-tu jouer?
   Bonhomm', Bonhomm', sais-tu jouer?
   Sais-tu jouer de ce flûte-là?
   Sais-tu jouer de ce flûte-là?
   Flût', flût', flût' de cett' flût' qui flûte!
   Flût', flût', flût' de cett' flût' qui flûte!
   Zing, zing, zing de ce violon-là!
   Zing, zing, zing de ce violon-là!
   Bonhomm'!
   Tu n'es pas maîtr' dans ta maison
   Quand nous y sommes!

3. Bonhomm', Bonhomm', sais-tu jouer?
   Bonhomm', Bonhomm', sais-tu jouer?
   Sais-tu jouer de ce tambour-là?
   Sais-tu jouer de ce tambour-là?
   Boom, boom, boom de ce tambour-là!
   Boom, boom, boom de ce tambour-là!
   Flût', flût', flût' de cett' flût' qui flûte!
   Flût', flût', flût' de cett' flût' qui flûte!
   Zing, zing, zing de ce violon-là!
   Zing, zing, zing de ce violon-là!
   Bonhomm'!
   Tu n'es pas maîtr' dans ta maison
   Quand nous y sommes!

Everybody loves a sandwich! Once in a while, Fred carries lunch in his backpack, and his sandwiches are always crammed with good things such as cheese, tomatoes, lettuce and sprouts.

46

# TEN FAT SAUSAGES

Traditional

1. Ten fat saus-a-ges siz-zlin' in the pan, Ten fat saus-a-ges siz-zlin' in the pan, If one goes "pop" and an-oth-er goes "bang", There'll be eight fat saus-a-ges siz-zlin' in the pan.

2. Eight fat sausages sizzlin' in the pan,
   Eight fat sausages sizzlin' in the pan,
   If one goes "pop" and the other goes "bang,"
   There'll be six fat sausages sizzlin' in the pan.

3. Six fat sausages sizzlin'…
   …four fat sausages sizzlin' in the pan.

4. Four fat sausages sizzlin'…
   …two fat sausages sizzlin' in the pan.

5. Two fat sausages sizzlin'…
   …no fat sausages sizzlin' in the pan.

6. No fat sausages sizzlin' in the pan,
   No fat sausages sizzlin' in the pan,
   If there's none to go "pop" and none to go "bang,"
   We'll have to buy more sausages to sizzle in the pan.

47

# The Dog and the Bone

*Based on an Aesop fable*

One day a hungry dog was passing by a butcher shop when she smelled a beautiful smell. Bones! The dog sneaked into the shop and there on the butcher's block she saw a lovely soup bone with some good meat on it. She snatched up the bone and ran off as fast as she could. The butcher ran after her, shouting and waving his meat cleaver.

With the big bone clamped between her teeth, the dog ran and ran, out of the town and into the country. At last she came to a little wooden bridge that crossed a river, and she stopped to catch her breath. There was no one following her. The butcher had given up the chase and gone back to his shop.

The dog looked over the bridge and saw her reflection in the water. What she saw made her growl.

"Who is that lucky dog with the big bone? Grrr. I want *that* bone too." She snarled and bared her teeth. She saw the dog in the water snarling back. She opened her mouth to make a grab for the other dog's bone, and of course her own bone fell into the water. So the hungry dog lost her bone and had nothing to eat that day.

*This is a song from Mexico about a pretty girl
called Cielito Lindo (Beautiful Sky).*

## CIELITO LINDO

Traditional

# How Peter Rabbit Got His Tail

*by Peg McKelvey*

Once upon a very long time ago, there was a beautiful clearing in the forest — something like Fred Penner's Place, only bigger. It had been built by Mother Nature, and many happy creatures lived there: Peter the rabbit, Rosie the skunk, Busy the beaver, and Mini the meadowmouse.

Most of these animals looked just about the same as they do now — all except the rabbit. In those bygone days, the rabbit had a long bushy tail. I suppose you think that a rabbit with a long bushy tail would look pretty funny! Well, you may laugh, but Peter Rabbit was very proud of his bushy tail, and he spent hours every day brushing it and cleaning it so that there were never any tangles or burrs in the soft fur.

One summer day, Peter Rabbit was hopping along beside the river when he happened to look over his shoulder and what do you suppose he saw? There, on the shiny surface of the water was a perfect picture of himself. It was just like looking in a mirror. But there was just one problem. In the mirror picture, Peter could not see his beautiful tail without getting a crick in his neck.

"Well, well," said Peter to himself. "There must be something I can do about that."

So Peter sat down and wiggled and waggled his back end, this way and that, until his beautiful tail hung down in just the right place, almost to the water's edge. Now he could see its reflection on the smooth surface of the water without cricking his neck.

So he sat there, and he sat there, admiring the reflection of his beautiful tail.

After a while, one of the little fishes that lived in the river came up to the surface and called to Peter in her tiny fishy voice.

"Peter! Peter!" called the little fish. "Don't hang your beautiful tail so close to the water. There is a big pike in this river, and it has very sharp teeth."

But Peter was not impressed. He said, "Go away, little fish. You are making ripples in the water and spoiling the picture of my beautiful tail."

So the little fish swam away, and Peter sat there beside the river, admiring his reflection. After a while, the hot sun made him sleepy, and he dozed off.

Then suddenly, there was a crack and a bang — a splash and a crunch! Peter woke up just in time to see the big pike sinking below the surface of the water with his beautiful bushy tail in its mouth.

"Oh, woe is me!" cried Peter Rabbit. "The nasty old pike has stolen my beautiful bushy tail."

Peter didn't know what to do, so he ran as fast as he could to Mother Nature's house to ask her to help him.

"Please, please, Mother Nature, will you *please* make me a new tail?"

"Well, now," said Mother Nature, "maybe I can, and maybe I can't. But what you need right now is a bandage on the place where your old tail used to be. Come into my house and I'll fix you up."

Mother Nature went to her medicine cupboard and found a ball of soft cotton and some adhesive tape. She put some disinfectant on the cotton and then taped it to the place where Peter's tail had been.

"Ouch!" yelled Peter. "That stuff stings!"

"It will help the sore place to get better," said Mother Nature. "Now off you go to your rabbit hole."

So Peter went home to his burrow, and after a while the sore place stopped hurting, and he went to sleep.

The next morning when Peter woke up, he found he had a new tail! It wasn't long and bushy like the old one. It was a little soft white tail, just like the cotton wool bandage that Mother Nature had taped on the day before.

And that is how Peter Rabbit became known as Peter Cottontail.

# SHOO, FLY, DON'T BOTHER ME

Traditional

Shoo, fly, don't both-er me, Shoo, fly, don't both-er me, Shoo, fly, don't both-er me, For

I be-long to some-bo-dy. I feel, I feel, I feel like a morn-ing star, I

feel, I feel, I feel like a morn-ing star, So, Shoo, fly, don't both-er me,

Shoo, fly, don't both-er me, Shoo, fly, don't both-er me, For I be-long to some-bo-dy.

53

# The Grasshopper and the Ants

*Based on a fable by Aesop*

One summer day, a grasshopper was hopping through the grass, chirping and singing merrily, when he noticed a whole colony of ants busy working. They were stowing away supplies of food for the winter — grains of corn, leaves, seeds and other things they had carefully dried in the sun.

"Why are you working so hard on a lovely summer day like this?" asked the grasshopper, as he danced carefree circles around them.

"Because winter will soon be coming," replied an ant, "and we want to make sure we have lots to eat during the long, cold days."

The grasshopper hopped up and down merrily. "That's silly," he said. "Winter's a long way away, and summer is for having fun!" With that, the grasshopper kicked up his heels and took off across the field, dancing and singing as he went.

Summer ended, autumn too, and winter came along as it always does. One cold day, when the ground was white with frost, the grasshopper appeared near the ant hill. But this time he didn't dance and he didn't sing. In fact, he could hardly hop, he was so thin and weak from hunger, and so cold from the frost and the bitter wind. "Please," he said to the ants. "Give me some of your food before I starve and freeze to death."

"We worked hard to gather our food," said one of the ants, "while you were singing and dancing the summer away!"

"You laughed at us then," said another ant. "Why don't you laugh and sing and dance the *winter* away, as well?"

So that was the end of the grasshopper, and the end of the story. Or was it?

Perhaps the ants were kind, and took pity on the grasshopper. Perhaps they decided to share their food with him, and so they saved his life. If that was so, then the grasshopper would surely be a different fellow from then on. He would dance and sing again, but only after the work was done!

Which ending do you like?

## Grasshoppers Three

Grasshoppers three a-fiddling went.
Hey! Ho! Never be still.
They paid no money toward their rent,
But all day long with elbow bent,
They fiddled a tune called Rillaby Rillaby,
Fiddled a tune called Rillaby Rill.

# GRASSHOPPER

Traditional

*Verse*

1. The first grass-hop-per jumped right ov - er the sec-ond grass-hop-per's back. Oh, the

first grass-hop-per jumped right ov - er the sec-ond grass-hop - per's back. The

first grass-hop-per jumped right ov - er the sec-ond grass-hop - per's back. Oh, the

first grass-hop-per jumped right ov - er the sec-ond grass-hop - per's back.

*Chorus*

2. One flea-fly flew up the flue
    and the other flea-fly flew down.
Oh, one flea-fly flew up the flue
    and the other flea-fly flew down.
One flea-fly flew up the flue
    and the other flea-fly flew down.
Oh, One flea-fly flew up the flue
    and the other flea-fly flew down.
*Chorus:* They were only playing leapfrog, etc.

### Peter, Peter

Peter, Peter, pumpkin-eater,
Had a wife and couldn't keep her;
He put her in a pumpkin shell,
And there he kept her very well.

### Jack and Jill

Jack and Jill went up the hill
To fetch a pail of water;
Jack fell down and broke his crown
And Jill came tumbling after.

Up Jack got, and home did trot
As fast as he could caper;
Went to bed to mend his head
With vinegar and brown paper.

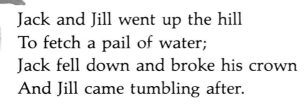

### Polly Put the Kettle On

Polly, put the kettle on,
Polly, put the kettle on,
Polly, put the kettle on,
We'll all have tea.

58

### Mary Ann McCarthy

Mary Ann McCarthy went a-fishing for some clams,
Mary Ann McCarthy went a-fishing for some clams,
Mary Ann McCarthy went a-fishing for some clams,
But she didn't get a single clam.

All she got was influenza!
All she got was influenza!
All she got was influenza!
But she didn't get a single clam.

### Diddle, Diddle, Dumpling

Diddle, diddle, dumpling, daughter Kate,
Went to bed in a dreadful state;
She wore a ribbon and a roller skate,
Diddle, diddle, dumpling, daughter Kate.

59

*Everyone has a name and some names rhyme with others — like Jack and Mac, Bonnie and Ronnie, Jill and Bill.*

*Here's a song with dozens of rhyming names. Perhaps you can think of more!*

## THE NAME SONG

Words by Pat Patterson
Music: Traditional

1. There's Ma - ry and Ga - ry, and Dar - ren and Ka - ren, And Ed - dy and Ted - dy, and San - dra and Sue. There's Ar - ty and Mar - ty, And Bel - la and Stel - la, and

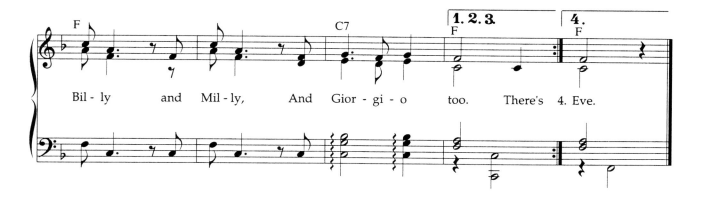

Bil - ly and Mil - ly, And Gior - gi - o too. There's 4. Eve.

2. There's Bonnie and Ronnie,
   And Ryan and Brian,
   And Harry and Larry,
   And Mae and Michelle.
   There's Doris and Morris,
   And Eric and Derek,
   And Clara and Sarah,
   And Wendy as well.

3. There's Chico, Enrico,
   And Peter and Dieter,
   And Pepe, Giuseppe,
   And Lara and Lise.
   There's Gina, Kristina,
   And Rudi and Trudi,
   And Tyler and Cuyler,
   And Mary-Louise.

4. There's Randy and Sandy,
   And Wally and Dolly,
   And Sherrill and Meryl,
   And Sidney and Steve.
   There's Annie and Danny,
   And Carol and Darryl,
   And Amy and Jamie,
   And Edith and Eve.

*You'll see the letter "S" dozens of times in this story. As you read it, you can have fun saying each "S" with a hissing sound.*

# Snodgrass and Mr. Sneer

*by Peg McKelvey*

Once upon a Saturday there was a schoolboy named Steve Smith who had a pet grass snake called Snodgrass. Some people are scared of snakes, but Steve loved Snodgrass, who was a sweet-natured special sort of snake.

Now Mr. Sneer, who lived next door, *detested* snakes. Whenever he saw Snodgrass he would say, "Snakes are slinky slippery slobs. If I catch that snake Snodgrass sleeping on my cellar steps, I will slosh it with soapy suds."

On Sunday, Snodgrass slipped away from Steve and slithered under the fence. Then he settled down to snooze in the sunshine on Mr. Sneer's cellar steps. Steve searched and searched for Snodgrass, but with no success.

Suddenly, Steve heard Mr. Sneer shouting. "I said I would slosh that snake with soapy suds, and so I shall!" he screeched. Then Steve knew that Snodgrass was snoozing in the sunshine on Mr. Sneer's cellar steps.

Steve slid under the fence, and saw Snodgrass sleeping in the sunshine. He sneaked up swiftly, snatched the snake and shoved him inside his shirt. Just then, Mr. Sneer came scurrying out with his soap suds. But, of course, Snodgrass was nowhere in sight.

That made Mr. Sneer sore. "Show me that snake so I can slosh him," screamed Mr. Sneer.

Steve stood still and spoke to Mr. Sneer. "Snake? What snake? Sorry, sir, but I see no snake. I suspect you must be seeing things."

Mr. Sneer was so furious that he started to sputter. "S-s-s-seeing things indeed! I s-s-s-saw a s-s-s-snake! For sure!"

While Mr. Sneer was sputtering and spluttering, Steve and Snodgrass slipped silently away and went home.

When he was safe and sound in his own house, Steve pulled Snodgrass out from under his shirt.

"Oh, Snodgrass, please don't snooze in the sunshine on Mr. Sneer's cellar steps *ever* again."

And Snodgrass said, "S-s-s-s-s-s-s-s," which is snake talk for . . . "Well, only on Sundays."

# SLITHERY SLATHERY SNAKE

2. I'm a slithery slathery snake,
   I'm a slithery slathery snake.
   When music I hear
   Is played sweet and clear,
   Then I slither and slather up straight.

# SKIP TO MY LOU

Lost my part - ner, what'-ll I do? Skip to my Lou, my dar - lin'.
I'll get a - noth-er one, pur-ti - er'n you, Skip to my Lou, my dar - lin'.

*Chorus*

Lou, Lou, Skip to my Lou. Lou, Lou, Skip to my Lou.

Lou, Lou, Skip to my Lou. Skip to my Lou, my dar - lin'.

3. Little red wagon, painted blue,
Little red wagon, painted blue,
Little red wagon, painted blue,
Skip to my Lou, my darlin'.
*Chorus:* Lou, Lou, etc.

4. Fly in the sugar-bowl, shoo, fly, shoo,
Fly in the sugar-bowl, shoo, fly, shoo,
Fly in the sugar-bowl, shoo, fly, shoo,
Skip to my Lou, my darlin'.
*Chorus:* Lou, Lou, etc.

5. Cows in the cornfield, two by two...

6. Rats in the bread-tray, how they chew...

7. One old boot and a run-down shoe...

8. Gone again, what'll I do?

# The Tortoise and the Hare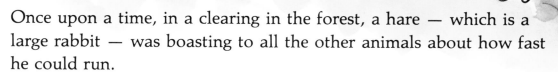

*Based on a fable by Aesop*

Once upon a time, in a clearing in the forest, a hare — which is a large rabbit — was boasting to all the other animals about how fast he could run.

"I'm faster than all of you!" he said. "Not one of you can run at the speed I can go!"

The other animals knew that the hare might well be right, because he certainly could run like the wind, so they didn't bother to argue with him. And since it seemed to make him happy, they just let him go on bragging about his great speed. The hare became rather

boring after a while, though, and after he had mentioned his
speediness ten times, a tortoise, who was counting, spoke up and said,
"Maybe you'd like to run a race."

"A race with *you*?" said the hare. "You must be making a joke!
Everyone knows you're one of the slowest creatures on earth!"

What he said was true, since the tortoise and its swimming
cousin, the turtle, do move very slowly.

But the tortoise insisted. "We'll see about that," she said. "That is,
if you're not afraid to race with me."

The hare laughed so hard that he turned a somersault. "All right,"
he said. "We'll run a race so I can show you that I'm the fastest runner
in the world."

"I bet *I'll* win," said the tortoise, quietly, and all the animals
laughed at that.

Then the squirrels marked out a course for the race. It would start and end in the clearing, circling through the woods and around a meadow in between.

The tortoise and the hare waited side by side for the signal to start, until the fox shouted out, "One, two, three, go!" The hare shot forward with the speed of an arrow and was out of sight in seconds. Meanwhile, the pokey tortoise plodded along, inch by inch, step by step.

After a minute or two, the hare looked back and couldn't even *see* the tortoise. "Well, well," he said to himself, "just as I thought. I might as well relax and have a little rest." He sat down with his back against a tree, and fell fast asleep.

The tortoise crept along steadily, and after an hour or so, came to where the hare was slumped, snoring quietly. "Strange," thought the tortoise, "I guess the hare is exhausted from all that boasting!" And she passed on towards the finish line.

Some time later, the hare awoke with a start. "Where am I? What am I doing here?" he asked nobody in particular. Then he remembered the race. He jumped to his feet and tore on in the direction of the clearing, figuring that the tortoise would still be far behind him. He could continue his nap when he got to the finish.

But imagine the hare's surprise when he got to the clearing and saw that the tortoise was already there! What's more, the tortoise was having a nap! The fox declared the tortoise winner of the race, and all the animals (except the hare, who went home to bed in a snit) circled around the tortoise chanting, "Slow and steady wins the race. Slow and steady wins the race."

*The Wordbird says:*
What's the difference between HERE and THERE?

The letter "T"

# THE GRAND OLD DUKE OF YORK

Traditional

1. The grand old Duke of York, He had ten thou-sand men. He
when they were up they were up, And when they were down they were down, And

marched them up to the top of the hill, And marched them down a - gain. 2. And
when they were on - ly half - way up They were nei - ther up nor down.

*To get from here to there, you can run like*
*a hare, march like a soldier, or hop.*

## Hippity Hop

Hippity hop to the barber shop
To buy a stick of candy,
One for me and one for you
And one for sister Mandy.

## The Kangaroo

I'm Hoppity Hop, the kangaroo,
I'm Hoppity Hop, how do you do?
I hop on both legs, not one like you,
I'm Hoppity Hop, the kangaroo.

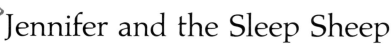

# Jennifer and the Sleep Sheep

*by Pat Patterson*

One bedtime as Jennifer lay in her bed,
Dozens of thoughts whirled 'round in her head.
She thought of the games she'd been playing that day,
And thought of her aunt who was coming to stay.

She thought of the swings and the pool in the park.
She thought of the time she'd stayed out after dark.
She hummed a sweet tune that her mother had sung.
She wiggled her ears and she stuck out her tongue.

She whispered a verse about Little Bo-Peep.
The thing she did *not* do was go off to sleep.
She tossed and she turned and she wriggled and rolled.
She thought she was hot, then she thought she was cold.

She jiggled her bed and it made such a din
The bedroom door opened and Father came in.
When Jennifer told him she just couldn't sleep,
Her father said sternly, "Well, try counting sheep!

"Imagine the sheep are jumping a fence
And don't stop to think that it doesn't make sense,
Just count every sheep as it leaps in the air.
As soon as one's gone there's another one there!"

"Yes, Dad," said Jennifer, closing her eyes,
"I'll *try* to imagine." And to her surprise
A sheep cleared a fence with a run and a jump,
A second sheep landed, bumpety-bump.

70

"That's two," said Jennifer, "Now three and four!
I have to keep counting 'cause here come some more!"
She counted to ten and then to fifteen;
She counted more sheep than she ever had seen.

Then one little sheep who had followed his friend,
Refused to leap over and ran 'round the end.
Should this one be counted? P'raps no and p'raps yes.
But Jennifer counted him nevertheless.

And soon there were thirty, and then forty-four,
But Jennifer knew that she couldn't count more,
So, drowsy and dreamy from counting the sheep,
She murmured, "Goodnight, Dad," and went off to sleep.

## Baa, Baa, Black Sheep

Baa, baa, black sheep, have you any wool?
Yes sir, yes sir, three bags full.
One for my master, and one for my dame,
And one for the little boy who lives down the lane.

## Little Boy Blue

Little Boy Blue, come blow your horn,
The sheep's in the meadow, the cow's in the corn;
But where is the boy that looks after the sheep?
He's under a haystack, fast asleep.

## Little Bo-Peep

Little Bo-Peep has lost her sheep,
And can't tell where to find them;
Leave them alone and they'll come home
And bring their tails behind them.

Then up she took her little crook,
Determined for to find them;
She found them indeed, but it made her heart bleed,
For they'd left their tails behind them.

It happened one day, as Bo-Peep did stray
Into a meadow close by;
She spied their tails side by side,
All hung on a tree to dry.

Then she heaved a sigh, and wiped her eye,
And ran over hill and dale-o,
And tried what she could, as a shepherdess should,
To tack each sheep to its tail-o.

# ROLL OVER! (TEN IN THE BED)

Traditional

Nine in the bed and the little one said:
"Roll over! Roll over!"
They all rolled over and one fell out.

Eight in the bed...

Seven in the bed...

Six in the bed...

Five in the bed...

Four in the bed...

Three in the bed...

Two in the bed...

One in the bed and the little one said:
*(spoken)* "Alone at last!"

# The Princess and the Pea

*Based on a story by Hans Christian Andersen*

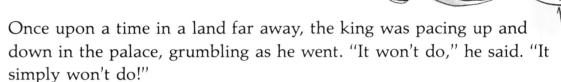

Once upon a time in a land far away, the king was pacing up and down in the palace, grumbling as he went. "It won't do," he said. "It simply won't do!"

"What won't do?" asked the queen. "And would you please stop marching back and forth. It's making me dizzy to watch you!"

The king stopped and faced her.

"It won't do not to have any grandchildren!" he said. "That's what won't do. There's our son, a handsome prince and a grown-up man. It's time he got married, settled down and helped to get us some grandchildren."

"I'm trying, Father," said the prince. "I just haven't been able to find the right princess."

"What's wrong with them all?" asked the king. "Surely among the dozens and dozens of princesses of all ages, shapes, sizes and colours who have come and gone in the last month, there must have been *one* who was just perfect for you!"

"Not one," said the prince. "If a princess was perfect in the way she looked, she was horrid in the way she behaved — or the other way around. If she was perfect in both looks and behaviour, it would turn out that she wasn't a real princess at all!"

"Well, keep looking," ordered the king. "And make it snappy!"

"Yes, Father," said the prince. "I'll start looking again in the morning. Right now it's raining."

"Very well," said the king. "First thing in the morning. Now I'm going to bed." And off he marched.

A few minutes later, as the prince and the queen talked about how hard it was to find a perfect princess these days, they were interrupted by a loud knock at the great palace door.

"Who one earth could that be?" asked the queen.

"Maybe it's Princess Right!" exclaimed the prince, hopefully.

"Nonsense!" snorted the queen. "No respectable princess would be out at this time of night. Why, when *I* was a princess . . ."

But the queen stopped before saying another word, because she heard the great door open, then footsteps coming near. She and the prince stood perfectly still, waiting.

Into the room there came a lovely young princess. Even though the rain had got her so wet that she made a puddle on the palace floor, the prince was delighted. "She's perfect!" he exclaimed.

"Her hair is very straight," observed the queen. "Princesses usually have wavy hair."

"She's been out in the rain, Mother," said the prince. "Besides, straight hair is very fashionable this season."

"I've come to marry the prince, Your Majesty," said the princess. "Splendid!" said the queen. "I shall go and prepare the guest room. Why don't you two young people go and make some hot chocolate?"

So the prince and the princess went to the kitchen while the queen got her chambermaids to prepare a bed for the princess.

Now the queen had a plan. She was going to prove whether or not this was a *real* princess. On the floor of the guest room she put a tiny green pea. It was so small you could hardly see it. On top of the pea, the chambermaids put ten mattresses. "More!" cried the queen, and ten more mattresses went on top. "And twenty feather beds!" she said. "There! Only a real princess would have such tender skin that she could feel a tiny pea under twenty mattresses and twenty feather beds. We'll know in the morning if she's a real princess or not!"

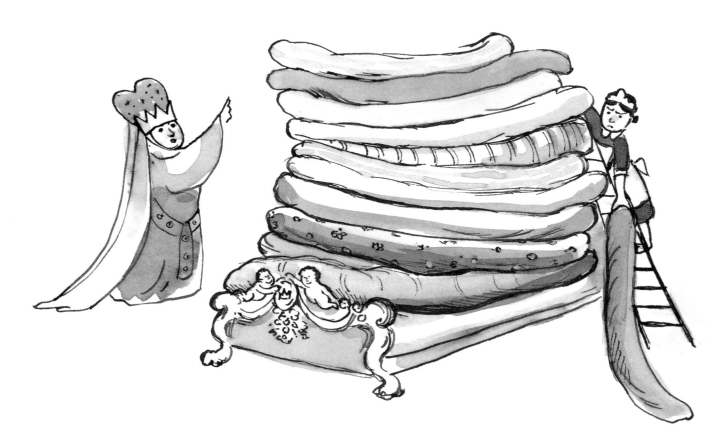

So the princess went to bed on top of all those mattresses and feather beds, and in the morning when she got up and went downstairs, the king, queen and prince were all waiting eagerly to see her.

"How did you sleep?" asked the queen.

"Were you comfortable?" enquired the prince.

"Well?" grumped the king.

"Oh dear," said the princess. "I'm afraid I had a terribly restless night. There was a hard, round bump under my bed and I was so uncomfortable I hardly slept a wink!"

"Hooray!" shouted the prince.

"Glad to hear it!" said the queen.

"Congratulations!" said the king.

They all knew that a real princess — a perfect princess — had arrived at last! Needless to say, the prince and princess made immediate plans to live happily ever after and to have some grandchildren for the king and queen.

### Six Green Peas

Six green peas in a pea-pod grew,
Three for me and three for you.
Crisp and sweet,
So good to eat,
Mine are gone and yours are too.

Once in a while, Dilly Duck comes to visit "Fred Penner's Place." He never stays long because he is always in a hurry to get back to the pond on the far side of the woods. You see, wild ducks like to eat often, and much of the food they eat is under water.

Dilly is a mallard duck, and mallards belong to a large family known as dabbling ducks. They don't dive into a pond for food; they just paddle along on top, dabbling or dipping their heads and necks under the water to get things to eat. Like most dabbling ducks, Dilly likes to eat leaves and seeds of water plants. He also eats worms, insects and tiny fishes. When mosquitoes lay their eggs on the water, ducks like Dilly do us a favour — they eat the tiny larvae that come out of the eggs before they can grow into big buzzy mosquitoes that bite. Thanks, Dilly.

## Five Little Ducks

Five little ducks went swimming one day,
Over the pond and far away,
Mother Duck said, "Quack, quack, quack, quack,"
But only four little ducks came back.

Four little ducks went swimming one day,
Over the pond and far away,
Mother Duck said, "Quack, quack, quack, quack,"
But only three little ducks came back.

Three little ducks went swimming one day,
Over the pond and far away,
Mother Duck said, "Quack, quack, quack, quack,"
But only two little ducks came back.

Two little ducks went swimming one day,
Over the pond and far away,
Mother Duck said, "Quack, quack, quack, quack,"
But only one little duck came back.

One little duck went swimming one day,
Over the pond and far away,
Mother Duck said, "Quack, quack, quack, quack,"
And five little ducks came swimming back!

## The Race

The hen went cluck
And the duck went quack,
As they raced around
And around the track,
And by the time they both came back,
The duck went cluck
And the hen went quack!

# SIX LITTLE DUCKS

Traditional

*Verse*

1. Six lit - tle ducks that I once knew, Fat ones, skin-ny ones,

fair ones too, But the one lit - tle duck with the feath - er on his back,

He led the oth - ers with a quack, quack, quack. Quack, quack, quack.

Quack, quack, quack. He led the oth-ers with a quack, quack, quack.

2. Down to the river they would go,
   Wibble wobble, wibble wobble, to and fro,
   But the one little duck with the feather on his back,
   He led the others with a quack, quack, quack.
   *Chorus:* Quack, quack, quack, etc.

3. Home from the river they would come,
   Wibble wobble, wibble wobble, ho hum hum,
   But the one little duck with the feather on his back,
   He led the others with a quack, quack, quack.
   *Chorus:* Quack, quack, quack, etc.

4. Six little ducks that I once knew,
   Fat ones, skinny ones, fair ones too,
   But the one little duck with the feather on his back,
   He led the others with a quack, quack, quack.
   *Chorus:* Quack, quack, quack, etc.

# Henny Penny

*Retold by Janis Nostbakken*

Once upon a time there lived a chicken whose name was Henny Penny. She spent most of every day scratching for food in the farm-yard. One day, when she was busily looking for some lunch, Henny Penny wandered under a big oak tree, and she got quite a shock when an acorn fell from the tree and landed — kerplunk — right on her head. Not knowing much about trees or acorns, Henny Penny thought that the sky must be falling, and decided she had better run to tell the king.

"Buck-buck-buck-buh*cock*!" she cried as she went along. "Look out! The sky is falling!"

Henny Penny went along and went along until she met Goosey Lucy, who asked her where she was going in such a hurry.

"Buck-buck-buck-buh*cock*! I'm going to tell the king the sky is falling!" Henny Penny replied, and Goosey Lucy thought she'd go along too. So Goosey Lucy and Henny Penny went along and went along until they met Ducky Lucky, who asked where they were going.

"Buck-buck-buck-buh*cock*! We're going to tell the king the sky is falling!" Henny Penny replied, and Ducky Lucky thought she'd go along too. So Ducky Lucky and Goosey Lucy and Henny Penny went along and went along until they met Turkey Lurkey, who asked where they were going.

"Buck-buck-buck-buh*cock*! We're going to tell the king the sky is falling!" Henny Penny replied, and Turkey Lurkey thought she would go along too. So Turkey Lurkey, Ducky Lucky, Goosey Lucy and Henny Penny went along and went along until they met Foxy Woxy, who asked where they were going.

"Buck-buck-buck-buh*cock*! We're going to tell the king the sky is falling!" Henny Penny replied.

82

Now Foxy Woxy was a clever fellow and a hungry one too. He saw his chance to have a delicious dinner of turkey and duck and goose and chicken, so he slyly said to the feathered friends, "I know a shortcut to get to the king's palace. Just follow me." And he led the way, not to a shortcut to the palace, but into a dark cave.

Turkey Lurkey had stepped inside; so had Ducky Lucky and Goosey Lucy, but for some reason Henny Penny sensed danger, and hesitated outside the cave. Just as the fox was about to pounce on her friends, she cried out, "Buck-buck-buck-buh*cock*! Look out!"

In a flash, Turkey Lurkey, Ducky Lucky and Goosey Lucy turned tail and fled from the cave. Just in time, too! They flapped and they flew right back to the safety of the farmyard, leaving the fox behind.

Henny Penny and her friends never did make their way to the king, but it didn't matter, because they could see that the sky was not falling after all. For that matter, it's still up there today. As for Turkey Lurkey, Ducky Lucky, Goosey Lucy and Henny Penny, they lived happily ever after.

### Cock-a-Doodle-Doo!

Cock-a-doodle-doo!
My dame has lost her shoe,
My master's lost his fiddle-stick,
And doesn't know what to do.

Cock-a-doodle-doo!
My dame has found her shoe,
And master's found his fiddle-stick,
Cock-a-doodle-doo!

Cock-a-doodle-doo!
My dame shall dance with you,
My master's found his fiddle-stick,
Cock-a-doodle-doo!

# TRY, TRY AGAIN

Words by Pat Patterson
Music:Traditional

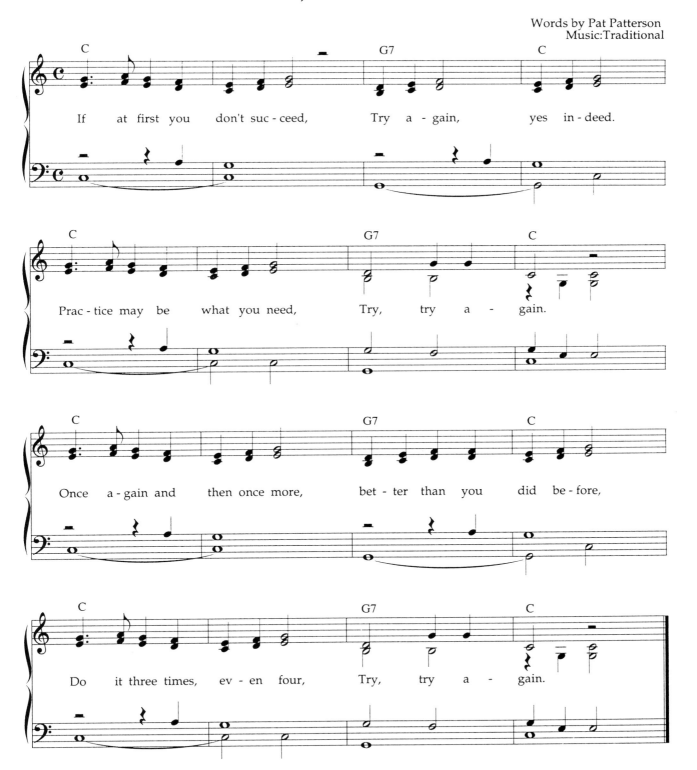

If at first you don't suc - ceed, Try a - gain, yes in - deed.

Prac - tice may be what you need, Try, try a - gain.

Once a - gain and then once more, bet - ter than you did be - fore,

Do it three times, ev - en four, Try, try a - gain.

# I HAD A ROOSTER

Traditional

**1.** Well, I had a roo - ster, my roo - ster pleased me, I

fed my roo - ster 'neath the green - wood tree, And

*Repeat for animal noises as dictated.*

my old roo - ster went cock - a - doo - dle - doo, De -

doo - dle, de - doo - dle, de - doo - dle, de - doo!

*Optional: Vamp 'til ready!!*

(2. Well,)

*Fine*

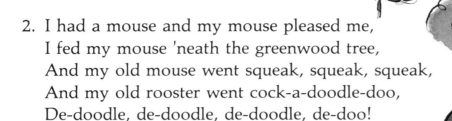

2. I had a mouse and my mouse pleased me,
   I fed my mouse 'neath the greenwood tree,
   And my old mouse went squeak, squeak, squeak,
   And my old rooster went cock-a-doodle-doo,
   De-doodle, de-doodle, de-doodle, de-doo!

3. I had a cat and my cat pleased me,
   I fed my cat 'neath the greenwood tree,
   And my old cat went meow, meow, meow,
   And my old mouse went squeak, squeak, squeak,
   And my old rooster went cock-a-doodle-doo,
   De-doodle, de-doodle, de-doodle, de-doo!

4. I had a dog and my dog pleased me,
   I fed my dog 'neath the greenwood tree,
   And my old dog went woof, woof, woof,
   And my old cat went meow, meow, meow,
   And my old mouse went squeak, squeak, squeak,
   And my old rooster went cock-a-doodle-doo,
   De-doodle, de-doodle, de-doodle, de-doo!

5. I had a cow and my cow pleased me,
   I fed my cow 'neath the greenwood tree,
   And my old cow went moo, moo, moo,
   And my old dog went woof, woof, woof,
   And my old cat went meow, meow, meow,
   And my old mouse went squeak, squeak, squeak,
   And my old rooster went cock-a-doodle-doo,
   De-doodle, de-doodle, de-doodle, de-doo!

6. I had a lion and my lion pleased me,
   I fed my lion 'neath the greenwood tree,
   And my old lion went roar, roar, roar,
   And my old cow went moo, moo, moo,
   And my old dog went woof, woof, woof,
   And my old cat went meow, meow, meow,
   And my old mouse went squeak, squeak, squeak,
   And my old rooster went cock-a-doodle-doo,
   De-doodle, de-doodle, de-doodle, de-doo!

# SOUP

Words by Pat Patterson
Music: Traditional Scottish

*Verse*

1. When ev - er I'm tir - ed or grum-py, _____ I know just the cure for my

state, Don't care if it's smooth or it's lum - py, _____ It's

soup that will make me feel great! Sou - oup,

sou - oup, There's noth-ing more sup-er than soup, good soup. Sou -

-oup, Sou - oup, There's noth-ing more sup-er than soup. _____

2. Chop veggies left over from supper,
   And mix with some broth in a pot,
   For soup that's a real filler-upper,
   Delicious to eat when it's hot.
   *Chorus:* Soup, soup, etc.

3. I tell you, the great joy of cooking
   Is tasting the things that you make.
   It's easy to tell without looking
   If you're eating a soup or a cake.
   *Chorus:* Soup, soup, etc.

4. Good soup is nutritious and yummy.
   Each spoonful you sip from your plate,
   As soon as it lands in your tummy,
   Will make you so glad that you ate
   *Chorus:* Soup, soup, etc.

# Stone Soup

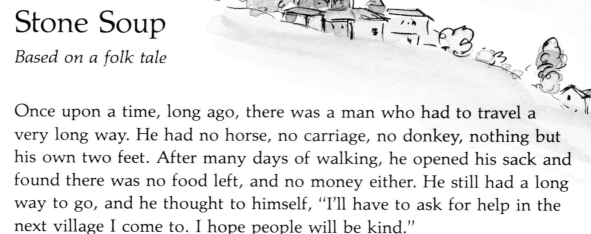

*Based on a folk tale*

Once upon a time, long ago, there was a man who had to travel a very long way. He had no horse, no carriage, no donkey, nothing but his own two feet. After many days of walking, he opened his sack and found there was no food left, and no money either. He still had a long way to go, and he thought to himself, "I'll have to ask for help in the next village I come to. I hope people will be kind."

When he came to the first house in the village a wonderful smell drifted out of the windows. Somebody was making a stew! "I've certainly chosen the right place," thought the traveller. "Surely they can spare me a plateful!"

But when he knocked at the door, a woman's angry voice shouted, "Go away, whoever you are! I'm busy!" So the traveller went on, disappointed and hungry.

A little farther on, seeing a farmer at work in his field, the traveller went up to the fence. "Excuse me, sir," he called.

"No excuses!" shouted the farmer. "Can't you read the sign? It says NO TRESPASSING, so away you go!"

Disheartened and hungrier than before, the traveller went on his way. He tried another house, and once again was curtly turned away. "What a strange place," he thought, "without one kind soul willing to help me."

Tired and hungrier than ever, the traveller stumbled on, until something he saw by the roadside gave him an idea. It was a big iron pot, lying in the ditch, and although it was a bit rusty and badly dented, it didn't seem to have any holes in it.

There was a creek nearby, and the traveller sluiced the pot out to clean it, then filled it with the clear, cold water. There were no leaks, so he gathered sticks and made a fire. When the water in the pot was boiling, the traveller got a big, smooth stone and dropped it into the pot. From his sack he took a big spoon, and began stirring, slowly and steadily.

A few minutes later, the angry woman who had been making stew came by on her way to market. She stopped and stared at the traveller and his iron pot as he went on stirring the water with the big stone in it.

"What on earth are you doing?"

"I am making stone soup, madam," said the traveller, pleasantly. "One of my favourites."

"Stone soup indeed!" said the woman. "How ridiculous!" And she walked on, muttering to herself.

Not long after that, the farmer who had shouted at the traveller to go away came by on his horse.

"What do you think you're doing?" he asked.

"I am making stone soup, sir," said the traveller, pleasantly. "One of my favourites."

"Never heard of such a thing," said the farmer, and he dug a heel into his horse's side to make it move on.

When a young woman with a baby stopped to inquire, she laughed at the traveller's answer, and others who passed either sneered or mumbled that the traveller must be crazy. Who ever heard of stone soup?

Later on, the farmer came back on his way home, and stopped to ask, half joking, "Uh, how does your stone soup taste?"

"It's good, sir," the traveller told him, "although it needs a little extra flavouring. Perhaps a carrot would make the difference."

Now the farmer just happened to have a sack of carrots tied across his horse's back, so he reached in, somewhat grudgingly, pulled out a single carrot and gave it to the traveller. "There's your carrot," he said, and rode on.

"Thank you, sir, thank you indeed," said the traveller, calling after him. "That will make it much better, I'm sure." With that, the traveller washed the carrot in the creek, broke it in pieces and dropped it into the pot.

A few minutes later, the angry woman came along, carrying all the things she had bought at the market. She stopped and sniffed at the traveller's iron pot. "Well, how does it taste?" she asked.

"Not quite right yet," answered the traveller. "It needs the special flavour of green leaves — preferably cabbage leaves. If only I had some!"

"If you need them so badly," said the woman grumpily, "I suppose I could let you have some of the outside leaves from the cabbage I got in the market."

"That would be splendid," said the traveller, as the woman tore off some of the coarse outside leaves and handed them to him. "Thank you very much indeed, madam."

The woman went on her way, while the traveller rinsed the cabbage leaves in the creek and dropped them into the pot. Then the woman stopped and called over her shoulder. "When will your stone soup be ready?"

"About an hour from now," said the traveller. "Do come by and try it."

One by one, the others who had laughed or sneered at the traveller and his stone soup passed by once more. They all asked the same question, "How does it taste?" and got the same answer — that it needed just a little extra something. And one by one, they added something to the pot — an onion, then a parsnip, a few potatoes, and a handful of beans. The passers-by were all so curious about this strange man and his stone soup that they didn't stop to think what was happening. If they had, they would have realized they had been tricked into giving the traveller all the things needed to make good *vegetable* soup. They might have realized, too, that the soup would be ready in less than another hour. Indeed, it was ready in *half* an hour.

It was thick and delicious, and the hungry traveller ate and ate until he was full. As he was about to shoulder his sack and walk on, he noticed that he had eaten *all* the soup; there was nothing left for the people who planned to come back and taste it. Then the traveller remembered how mean they had been when he was tired and hungry, telling him to go away, sneering and laughing at him.

He took the pot to the creek and sluiced it out. He put the big, smooth stone inside, filled the pot once again with the cold, clear water, and placed it on the embers of the fire. Then he picked up his sack and set off down the road, allowing himself a little smile.

"Well," he thought, "I did leave those people with something very valuable — my recipe for stone soup!"

# Bubba's Bath

*by Janis Nostbakken*

Once upon a time there was a sheepdog named Bubba. She was a big, floppity-flop dog with long, shaggy hair, and when she ran, her four furry paws went loppity-lop, loppity-lop. Bubba's favourite place to play was a field right next to the house where she lived with her family. She liked to roll in the grass, to bury bones in the dirt, and to join in games of tag and hide-and-seek with the neighbourhood children.

But one thing Bubba did not like was a bath. Because she spent so much time rolling and digging and playing outdoors, she got very dirty. Her long, shaggy hair had once been as white and fluffy as snow, but now her fur was matted and knotted and the white had turned to dingy gray. Bubba needed a bath!

The family tried one thing after another to get her clean. On a warm day, they set the sprinkler on the lawn. The children ran through the water and tried to coax Bubba to join them.

"Come on, Bubba! It's fun!" they cried. But Bubba wouldn't budge.

Another day they filled a big tin tub with water and tossed in one of Bubba's favourite toys, hoping she would dive in after it.

"Get it, Bubba! Get your rubber ducky!" But Bubba wouldn't budge.

They thought they might solve the problem by washing the car. Bubba loved the car and was always ready to go for a drive.

"Come on, Bubba, let's go!" they called. "Here, Bubba, good dog." But Bubba wouldn't budge.

What was to become of her? She couldn't stay dirty for ever and ever.

One morning Bubba was dozing in a sunny spot in the back yard, when all of a sudden, she felt something tickle her nose. It was a big, beautiful bubble! Bubba had never seen anything so lovely. It was clear and shiny and perfectly round, and Bubba wanted to play with it. But when she leapt up, the bubble burst and disappeared. Where did it go?

A moment later, Bubba saw another bubble. This time it was floating through the air over her head. She just had to chase it, but when she tried to catch the bubble, it popped.

Soon there were lots of bubbles floating around the yard — big ones, small ones, even double bubbles! It was so exciting that Bubba raced after them, jumping and barking with glee. Before she knew it, she was running straight for a tub full of bubbles. Loppity-loppity-lop! Splash! With one large leap, Bubba landed smack in the middle of a bubble bath. Her family had played a trick on her. They'd filled the wading pool with water and added sudsy soap that made oodles of bubbles.

Bubba couldn't resist those pretty bubbles, so there she was, splishing and splashing and having a bath at last!

# THIS IS THE WAY

Traditional

1. This is the way we bath the dog, bath the dog, bath the dog,

This is the way we bath the dog, So ear - ly in the morn - ing.

2. This the way we sweep the floor,
   Sweep the floor, sweep the floor,
   This is the way we sweep the floor,
   So early in the morning.

3. This is the way we iron our clothes,
   Iron our clothes, iron our clothes,
   This is the way we iron our clothes,
   So early in the morning.

4. This is the way we brush our teeth,
   Brush our teeth, brush our teeth,
   This is the way we brush our teeth,
   So early in the morning.

5. This is the way we comb our hair,
   Comb our hair, comb our hair,
   This is the way we comb our hair,
   So early in the morning.

*It's fun to make up your own verses
about things you do every day.*

*There are several other songs that
we can sing with this same tune.*

Here we go gathering nuts in May,
Nuts in May, nuts in May,
Here we go gathering nuts in May,
On a cold and frosty morning.

*Another question from the Wordbird:*
How do you catch a squirrel?

Climb up a tree and act like a nut.

# THE WORDBIRD SONG

Words by Peg McKelvey
Music by Joy Alexander

## The Little Turtle

There was a little turtle.
He lived in a box.
He swam in a puddle.
He climbed on the rocks.

He snapped at a mosquito.
He snapped at a flea.
He snapped at a minnow.
And he snapped at me.

He caught the mosquito.
He caught the flea.
He caught the minnow.
But he didn't catch me.

*Vachel Lindsay*

# THE PUDDLE SONG

Words by Dodi Robb and Pat Patterson
Music by Pat Patterson

Pud - dles are pud - dle - y, pud - dles are fun, The trou - ble with a

pud - dle is it dries in the sun.
1. You _____ can't take it
2. You _____ can't wrap it

Chorus: Puddles are puddley, etc.

3. Can't paint it red then give it to your mother,
   Can't fold it over or cut it in two.
   Can't take it for a walk like your baby brother
   'Cause a puddle can never go along with you.
   Chorus: Puddles are puddley, etc.

# IF YOU LOVE A HIPPOPOTAMUS

Words and Music by
Connie Kaldor

*Chorus*    C                             Am

If you love a hip-po-pot-a-mus, And you love ____ her a lot-ta-mus,

Dm                  G7                                  C *Fine*

She will be your friend, That can be might-y han-dy now and then.       'Cuz

*Chorus:* If you love a hippopotamus, etc.

2. If you want a cookie
   But it's too high on the shelf,
   You can climb on the back of a hippopotamus
   And get one for yourself.
   *Chorus:* If you love a hippopotamus, etc.

*Sing the tune of the verse twice for the next part.*

3. If you're put to bed
   And you find that you just can't sleep,
   Your friend the hippopotamus
   Into your room will creep.
   She'll sing a lullaby
   Till you begin to snore,
   Then she'll tiptoe out, hippopotamusly,
   And shut the door.
   *Chorus:* If you love a hippopotamus, etc.

# FOOBA WOOBA JOHN

Traditional

Saw a goat in a pink coat, Foo-ba woo-ba, foo-ba woo-ba,

Saw a goat in a pink coat, Foo-ba woo-ba, John.

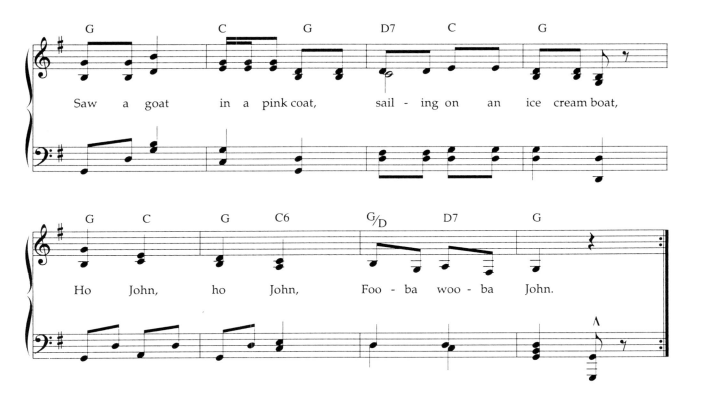

2. Met a fly in a pie,
Fooba wooba, fooba wooba,
Met a fly in a pie,
Fooba wooba John.
Met a fly in a pie,
He ate so much he thought he'd die,
Ho John, ho John,
Fooba wooba John.

3. Saw a whale on her tail,
Fooba wooba, fooba wooba,
Saw a whale on her tail,
Fooba wooba John.
Saw a whale on her tail
Eating pork chops by the pail,
Ho John, ho John,
Fooba wooba John.

4. Saw a crow flying low,
Fooba wooba, fooba wooba,
Saw a crow flying low,
Fooba wooba John.
Saw a crow flying low,
On his way to see a show,
Ho John, ho John,
Fooba wooba John.

5. Saw an elf on the shelf,
Fooba wooba, fooba wooba,
Saw an elf on the shelf,
Fooba wooba John.
Saw an elf on the shelf,
If you want some more, just
sing it yourself!
Ho John, ho John,
Fooba wooba John.

# Three Billy Goats Gruff

*Based on a Scandinavian folk tale*

Did you know that boy goats are called Billy Goats? Nobody seems to know why they're not called Michael Goats or Christopher Goats, or Matthew or Adam Goats, but that's the way it is. They're called Billy Goats, and this is a story about three of them. All three were members of the same family, known as Gruff, and they lived together in a wide valley.

Late one summer, there was very little green grass left in the valley, and the three Billy Goats Gruff were getting rather hungry. (Goats eat grass the way *we* eat lettuce or spinach or cabbage.) Far up the hillside, they could see a fine meadow with plenty of green grass, and they decided to go there right away.

"We'll be able to eat and eat," said Big Billy Goat Gruff.

"And eat some more," said Middle Billy Goat Gruff.

"And eat even more!" added Little Billy Goat Gruff. So off they went, and they trotted quickly along until they came to a rushing river. Luckily there was a wooden bridge over the river, but it was very old and rickety, so to be safe, they agreed it would be best to cross it one at a time.

"You first," said Big Billy Goat Gruff to the middle one. "I'm so big and heavy the bridge might break."

"Not me," said Middle Billy Goat Gruff. "I may not be as big as you, but I'm still pretty heavy."

"I'll go," said Little Billy Goat Gruff. "No problem." And off he trotted onto the bridge, which went "Rickety-Rack, Rickety-Rack" as he went across. Suddenly he stopped in his tracks, as a fierce, raspy voice shouted out, "Stop! Who dares to cross my bridge?"

It was the voice of a mean and ugly troll who lived under the bridge, and his words echoed through the valley as Little Billy Goat Gruff replied, "I'm just the smallest of the Billy Goats Gruff, and I'm going up to the green meadow to get something to eat."

"Oh no you're not," said the troll, "because *I'm* hungry too, and I'm going to eat *you*!"

"I'll give you a tip," said the littlest goat. "Just wait a minute until Middle Billy Goat Gruff comes and you'll get a much better meal than you would from *my* little body."

"Oh, all right," said the troll. "Get going!" So Little Billy Goat Gruff quickly scampered across the bridge and up to the green meadow.

A moment later, Middle Billy Goat Gruff stepped onto the bridge. "Rickety-Rack, Rickety-Rack" went the bridge, in time with his footsteps. "Stop! Who dares cross my bridge?" It was the troll, and Middle Billy Goat Gruff thought quickly.

"I'm Middle Billy Goat Gruff," he said, "just heading for the meadow up there, before I faint from hunger."

"Hunger!" snarled the troll. "*I'm* the one who's hungry around here. Just step right up so I can eat you!"

"If you're really so hungry," said the middle one, "I'll give you some really good advice. Just wait a minute, and you'll have the biggest, fattest, juiciest, most delicious goat you could ask for. Don't waste your time or teeth on scrawny, bony little me!"

"All right. Get out of my way and let me at him!" So Middle Billy Goat Gruff scampered across the bridge and up to the green meadow.

A moment later, Big Billy Goat Gruff stepped onto the bridge. "Rickety-Rack, Rickety-Rack" it went, as he put his feet down. "Stop! Who dares cross my bridge?" shouted the troll.

"It is I — the biggest, fattest, most delicious of all the Billy Goats Gruff. In fact, I am so big and fat and delicious that I'm going to give you a tip. You'd better not see me all at once. That would be bad for your digestion!"

"Aha! How shall I see you then?" asked the troll.

"First, turn your back," said Big Billy Goat Gruff. So the fierce, ugly troll turned around, and said, "Now what?"

"Now *this*!" said the big goat as he butted the troll with his strong horns and sent him somersaulting over and over and down into the river below. Then Big Billy Goat Gruff scampered across the bridge and up to the green meadow.

The other two were waiting for him in the middle of a patch of the greenest, sweetest grass they had ever tasted. So the three Billy Goats Gruff stayed in the meadow, eating the delicious grass and chuckling about the time they fooled the fierce troll and sent him down into the rushing river.

As far as anyone knows, they lived happily ever after.

*Here's a riddle from the Wordbird:*
When will the letter "G" surprise a farmer?

When it changes OATS to GOATS.

*They say goats will eat just about anything.*

## Mary Had a William Goat

Mary had a William goat,
William goat, William goat,
Mary had a William goat,
And he was lined with zinc.

One day he ate an oyster can,
Oyster can, oyster can,
One day he ate an oyster can,
And a kitchen sink.

## I Went to Visit a Farm

I went to visit a farm one day,
I saw a goat across the way,
And what do you think I heard it say?
Maaaa, maaaa, maaaa.

I went to visit a farm one day,
I saw a lamb across the way,
And what do you think I heard it say?
Baaaa, baaaa, baaaa.

I went to visit a farm one day,
I saw a cow across the way,
And what do you think I heard it say?
Moooo, moooo, moooo.

I went to visit a farm one day,
I saw a pig across the way,
And what do you think I heard it say?
Oink, oink, oink.

*You can make up more verses about other farm animals.*

*This is an echo song. Try singing it with two people or two groups of people.*

# GROGGIN'S GOAT

Traditional

1. There was a man (*There was a man*), Now please take note (*Now please take note*), There was a man (*There was a man*), Who had a goat (*Who had a goat*), He loved that goat (*He loved that goat*), In - deed he did (*In - deed he*

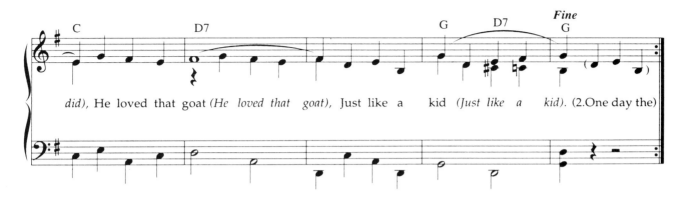

*did)*, He loved that goat *(He loved that goat)*, Just like a kid *(Just like a kid)*. *(2.One day the)*

2. One day the goat   *(One day the goat)*,
   Felt frisk and fine   *(Felt frisk and fine)*,
   Ate three red shirts   *(Ate three red shirts)*
   Right off the line   *(Right off the line)*.
   The man, he grabbed   *(The man, he grabbed)*
   Him by the back   *(Him by the back)*,
   And tied him to   *(And tied him to)*
   The railroad track   *(The railroad track)*.

3. Now, when that train   *(Now, when that train)*
   Hove into sight   *(Hove into sight)*,
   That goat grew pale   *(That goat grew pale)*
   And green with fright   *(And green with fright)*.
   He heaved a sigh   *(He heaved a sigh)*
   As if in pain   *(As if in pain)*,
   Coughed up the shirts   *(Coughed up the shirts)*
   And flagged the train   *(And flagged the train)*.

*This kind of song is called a nonsense song because its words make no sense at all!*

# THE HORSE NAMED BILL

Traditional
Additional lyrics by Pat Patterson

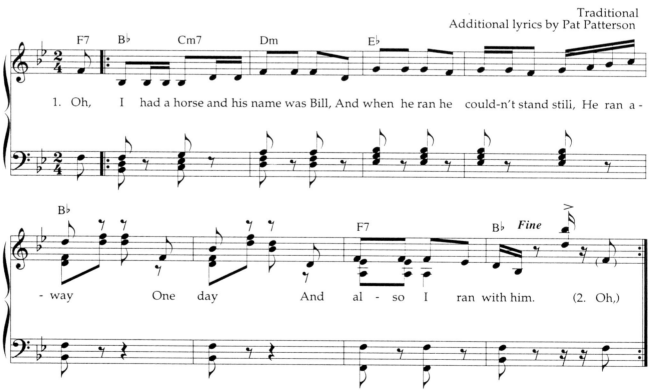

1. Oh, I had a horse and his name was Bill, And when he ran he could-n't stand stili, He ran a-way One day And al - so I ran with him. (2. Oh,)

2. Oh, he ran so fast he could not stop,
   He ran into a barber shop,
   And he fell
   Pell mell
   On the barber's left shoulder.

3. And while he was there, that horse named Bill,
   He combed his hair and swallowed a pill,
   And he sneezed
   And he wheezed
   And so did the barber.

4. He drank from the sink 'til he had his fill,
   Then sang like a bird with a twitter and a trill,
   And a chirp
   And a burp
   And how's your Uncle Charley?

5. He ran on home of his own free will,
   And cantered backwards up the hill,
   With a huff
   And a puff
   And a tangle in his tonsils.

6. So that's the tale of the horse named Bill.
   If it goes on longer it'll make you ill,
   So we say
   "Hey, hey!
   Just stop this nonsense right now!"

# The Magic Spaghetti Pot

*A retelling of the story "The Magic Porridge Pot"*

Once there was a little girl called Sabrina, who lived with her mother in a very small house. They were very poor, and sometimes they did not have enough money to buy food. Then Sabrina would go into the woods to search for nuts and berries.

One day, Sabrina searched everywhere but she couldn't find a single nut or berry. She sat down and cried.

"Cheer up!" said a strange crackly voice.

Sabrina jumped, and turned around.

Standing there was an old woman in a long black cloak. She was holding a little iron pot.

"This is a magic pot," said the old woman. "Take it home and put it on the fire. Then say the magic words. You must say, 'Boil, little pot, boil,' and it will fill up with delicious spaghetti. Can you remember what to say?"

"I must say 'Boil, little pot, boil,'" said Sabrina.

"That's right," said the old woman. "And when you have had all the spaghetti you can eat, you must say, 'Stop, little pot, stop!' and the magic pot will stop boiling. Now don't forget the magic words." Then the old woman disappeared.

Sabrina ran home. She put the pot on the fire and said, "Boil, little pot, boil!"

Sure enough, delicious spaghetti bubbled up, until there was enough for Sabrina and her mother. Then Sabrina said the other magic words, "Stop, little pot, stop!" And the magic pot stopped boiling.

One day, Sabrina went out to visit a friend. After a while, Sabrina's mother began to get hungry. She put the magic pot on the fire and said, "Boil, little pot, boil!" The pot began to bubble up with delicious spaghetti.

But Mother had forgotten the magic words to make the pot stop. Soon spaghetti was bubbling right over the top of the pot.

**114**

"Halt, pot, halt!" said Mother. But those were not the magic
words. The delicious spaghetti bubbled out of the pot and covered the
floor of the little house.

"No more, no more!" cried Mother. But those were not the magic
words. Lots and lots of delicious spaghetti rolled out the front door
and into the street.

Sabrina's mother rushed out of the house and ran down the street
shouting, "Cease, little pot, cease!" But mounds and mounds of
delicious spaghetti came down the street after her.

Sabrina's mother called, "Helllllllllp!"

Luckily, Sabrina heard her mother calling. She ran home and
spoke the magic words.

Can you remember what they are? Sabrina said, "Stop, little pot,
stop!" And the magic pot stopped.

Then everyone in the village came out into the street with spoons
and cups and buckets. They picked up all the delicious spaghetti.
There was enough for everyone to eat for days and days.

# MRS. MURPHY'S CHOWDER

Traditional

*Verse*

G                                                              D7

1. Won't you bring back, Won't you bring back, Mis - sus Mur - phy's chow-der? It was

D7                                                              G

tune - ful, ev' - ry spoon - ful  Made you yo - del  loud - er.

G                    D7              G                    D7

Af - ter din - ner, Un - cle Ben  Used to fill his  fount - ain pen

G      D7        G      Em        Am7      D7      G      *Chorus*

From a plate of Mis - sus Mur - phy's chow - der.  It had

2. Won't you bring back,
   Won't you bring back Missus Murphy's chowder?
   From each helping you'll be yelping
   For a headache powder.
   And if they have it where you are
   You might find a trolley car
   In a plate of Missus Murphy's chowder.
   *Chorus:* It had ice cream, cold cream, etc.

### Five Little Kittens

Five little kittens playing near the door;
One ran away and then there were four.

Four little kittens underneath a tree;
One heard a dog bark and then there were three.

Three little kittens thinking what to do;
One saw a little bird and then there were two.

Two little kittens sitting in the sun;
One ran to catch his tail and then there was one.

One little kitten looking for some fun;
He saw a butterfly and then there was none.

## Three Little Monkeys

Three little monkeys swinging in a tree,
Along came a crocodile as quiet as can be.
The first monkey said, "You can't catch me!"
Snap!

Two little monkeys swinging in a tree,
Along came a crocodile as quiet as can be.
The second monkey said, "You can't catch me!"
Snap!

One little monkey swinging in a tree,
Along came a crocodile as quiet as can be.
The third monkey said, "You can't catch me!"
Snap! Missed me!

## One Potato, Two Potato

One potato, two potato, three potato, four,
Five potato, six potato, seven potato, more!
Eight potato, nine potato, ten potato, then,
Pick them up and start again.

## The Fish

One, two, three, four, five,          (*Count on fingers.*)
Once I caught a fish alive.          (*Wiggle hand like a fish.*)
Six, seven, eight, nine, ten,        (*Count on fingers.*)
Then I let him go again.             (*Pretend to throw fish back.*)

Why did you let him go?
Because he bit my finger so.          (*Shake hand violently.*)
Which finger did he bite?
The little finger on the right.      (*Hold up finger.*)

# THE ANTS CAME MARCHING

Traditional

1. The ants come march-ing one by one, Hur - rah! _____ Hur - rah! _____ The

ants come march-ing one by one, Hur - rah! _____ Hur - rah! _____ The

ants come march-ing one by one, The lit - tle one stopped to suck his thumb. And they

all go march-ing down a - round the town. (Boom, boom, boom.) (The)

2. The ants came marching two by two, Hurrah! Hurrah!
   The ants came marching two by two, Hurrah! Hurrah!
   The ants came marching two by two,
   The little one stopped to tie his shoe.
   And they all go marching down around the town.
   (Boom, boom, boom.)

3. The ants came marching three by three, Hurrah! Hurrah!
   The ants came marching three by three, Hurrah! Hurrah!
   The ants came marching three by three,
   The little one stopped to climb a tree.
   And they all go marching down around the town.
   (Boom, boom, boom.)

4. The ants came marching four by four...
   The little one stopped to shut the door...

5. The ants came marching five by five...
   The little one stopped to take a dive...

6. The ants came marching six by six...
   The little one stopped to pick up sticks...

7. The ants came marching seven by seven...
   The little one stopped to go to heaven...

8. The ants came marching eight by eight...
   The little one stopped to shut the gate...

9. The ants came marching nine by nine...
   The little one stopped to scratch his spine...

10. The ants came marching ten by ten...
    The little one stopped to say, "The end!"

*Stop singing here!*

# The Rainbow in Lake Louise

*Adapted from a legend of the Stoney Indians*

A long time ago, the Stoney Indians lived and hunted in the valley of the Bow River, in Alberta.

There is a beautiful lake there called Lake Louise, surrounded by the gleaming snowfields and the shining peaks of the Rocky Mountains. The waters of the lake are emerald green, although sometimes its surface reflects the clear blue of the sky or the fiery red and gold of the sunset.

The Stoney Indians have a legend about how the lake captured all the colours of the rainbow. It is the story of a giant Indian chief called Black Crow.

One day, after a rain storm, Black Crow saw a brilliant rainbow in the sky. It was so beautiful that he wanted it for himself.

"If only I can catch that rainbow," said Black Crow, "I will make a magic bow from it."

So Black Crow went up the mountain and climbed to the top of a tall tree. From there he could touch the sky.

Black Crow reached out and took hold of the end of the rainbow. But as soon as he did, the rainbow began to melt and the colours ran down his fingers. Black Crow was so angry that he pulled the rainbow out of the sky and smashed it against the side of the mountain. The rainbow cracked into a thousand coloured pieces, and fell into the lake below.

The giant Indian came down from the mountain to search for the rainbow. He saw the coloured pieces at the bottom of the lake, but the water was so deep that he couldn't reach them.

The Great Spirit had to build a new rainbow to hold up the sky when it rains. But you can still see the old rainbow, there at the bottom of Lake Louise.

# ONE MORE RIVER

Traditional

3. The animals came in two by two,
There's one more river to cross.
The grizzly bear and the kangaroo,
There's one more river to cross.
*Chorus:* One more river, etc.

4. The animals came in three by three,
There's one more river to cross.
The tall giraffe and the tiny flea,
There's one more river to cross.
*Chorus:* One more river, etc.

5. The animals came in four by four,
There's one more river to cross.
The hippopotamus stuck in the door,
There's one more river to cross.
*Chorus:* One more river, etc.

6. The animals came in five by five,
There's one more river to cross.
The bees were using the bear
    as a hive,
There's one more river to cross.
*Chorus:* One more river, etc.

7. The animals came in six by six,
There's one more river to cross.
The monkey up to his usual tricks,
There's one more river to cross.
*Chorus:* One more river, etc.

8. The animals came in seven by seven,
There's one more river to cross.
Said the ant to the elephant,
    "Who're you shovin'?"
There's one more river to cross.
*Chorus:* One more river, etc.

9. The animals came in eight by eight,
There's one more river to cross.
Some of them early and some
    of them late,
There's one more river to cross.
*Chorus:* One more river, etc.

10. The animals came in nine by nine,
There's one more river to cross.
They marched in slowly in a line,
There's one more river to cross.
*Chorus:* One more river, etc.

11. The animals came in ten by ten,
There's one more river to cross.
If you want any more, I'll sing it again,
There's one more river to cross.
*Chorus:* One more river, etc.

Renée Raccoon sometimes visits "Fred Penner's Place," even though she has to miss some sleep to do it. Raccoons usually sleep in the daytime. Then at night, when most of us are asleep, they wake up and go hunting for food.

Renée is a good climber, like all raccoons, and her favourite place to sleep is on a high branch of a tree, where she curls up and feels perfectly safe.

A country raccoon like Renée often finds food on a farm and enjoys anything from corn to chickens. Or she may go into a river or a pond to catch crayfish for her meal. In the water, on the ground, or up a tree, a raccoon feels entirely at home.

# BILE THEM CABBAGE DOWN

Traditional

1. Rac - coon has a bush - y tail, 'Pos - sum's tail is bare,
*Chorus:* Bile them cab - bage down, down, Bake that hoe - cake brown, brown, The

Rab - bit's got no tail at all But a lit - tle bunch of hair.
on - ly song that I can sing Is bile them cab - bage down.

2. Raccoon and the possum
   Rackin' 'cross the prairie,
   Raccoon asked the possum,
   Did she plan to marry?
   *Chorus:* Bile them cabbage down, etc.

3. Possum is a cunning thing,
   She travels in the dark,
   And never thinks to curl her tail
   Till she hears old Rover bark.
   *Chorus:* Bile them cabbage down, etc.

4. Possum up a 'simmon tree,
   Raccoon on the ground,
   Raccoon say to the possum,
   "Won't you shake them 'simmons down?"
   *Chorus:* Bile them cabbage down, etc.

127

# The Raccoon
# Who Wanted to Be Queen

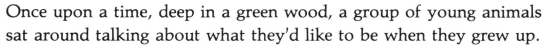

*by Pat Patterson*

Once upon a time, deep in a green wood, a group of young animals sat around talking about what they'd like to be when they grew up.

"I want to be an astronaut!" said a squirrel, and none of the others showed any surprise, because this young squirrel did quite a bit of flying through space already, when he jumped from one tree to another.

Then a groundhog spoke up. "When I grow up," she said proudly, "I'm going to be an archaeologist."

There was a stunned silence for a moment. Then all the animals shouted together, "An arkay-*what*?"

"An archaeologist," explained the groundhog earnestly, "is someone who digs away down into the ground, looking for things from long ago." And although none of the animals was quite sure what the groundhog was talking about, they believed her when she said that people learn a lot about olden times from what gets dug up. Besides, the groundhog was a very good digger, as everyone knew. She lived in a burrow at the end of a long tunnel under the ground, and she had dug every inch of it herself.

One by one, the animals told the others what he or she would like to be as a grownup. There was a deer — a young buck — who thought he'd like to be a great athlete, and certainly he was already a good jumper, who could run like the wind.

A mouse thought she'd like to work in a cheese factory, as a taster, trying out all the cheeses to make sure they were good before sending them to the grocery stores. The others laughed and told her she'd likely be fired from her job for eating too much.

A porcupine thought he could be a security guard at a bank, because no bank robber would take a chance on running into a porcupine's long, sharp quills.

Before long all the animals had spoken — except for one, and all eyes turned towards a raccoon named Renée. "Come on, Renée!" they shouted. "Don't be shy. Tell us what you'd like to be."

Renée Raccoon drew herself up to be as tall as she could. She paused for a second, looking around at all the other animals, then said in a very dignified voice, "When I grow up, I want to be Queen!"

"Queen!" exclaimed one. "Queen?" said another. "Queen!!" They were all absolutely flabbergasted. Queen Renée Raccoon? Suddenly a deep voice spoke from high up in a tree. "*Why* do you want to be Queen?"

It was a wise old owl, who must have been perched up there listening to everything that had been going on. Renée explained that she thought it would be really nice to live in a palace, and to wear a shiny crown on her head, and to have all sorts of important people bowing to her.

"A queen has to stay awake all day!" said the owl. (Raccoons like to *sleep* in the daytime and prowl about at night.) "And a queen has to shake hands with so many people that your paws would get sore. And what's more, a queen could never never never go rooting about in people's garbage cans!"

Well, that did it. You see, rooting in people's garbage cans in the dark of night is a raccoon's favourite sport. City raccoons do it all the time, and a country raccoon will walk miles to find a suburban garbage can with bits of leftover people-food in it.

"No garbage cans for a queen?" asked Renée in a shocked voice.

"No garbage cans for a queen," said the wise old owl. Everyone was silent for a few minutes while Renée thought about all this. Finally she looked up, squared her shoulders, and looking every bit as regal as any queen, she said, "I know what I'm going to be when I grow up. I have decided. I shall be a real . . . grown up . . . raccoon!"

Everyone cheered. They felt sure that she had made a good choice, and would live happily ever after.

# OLD MACDONALD HAD A FARM

Traditional

1. Old Mac-Don-ald had a farm, E - I - E - I - O, _____ And

on this farm he had a cow, E - I - E - I - O, With a

*Repeat for each new animal sound.*

F  Gm7  G#dim  F/A  F

moo - moo here and a  moo - moo there,  here a moo,  there a moo,  ev'- ry - where a moo - moo

F  B♭  F  F  C7  F  C7

Old Mac-Don-ald  had  a  farm,  E - I - E - I - O, _____

2. Old MacDonald had a farm, E-I-E-I-O,
   And on this farm he had a pig, E-I-E-I-O.
   With an oink-oink here and an oink-oink there,
   Here an oink, there an oink, everywhere an oink-oink,
   A moo-moo here, a moo-moo there,
   Here a moo, there a moo, everywhere a moo-moo,
   Old MacDonald had a farm, E-I-E-I-O.

3. Old MacDonald had a farm, E-I-E-I-O,
   And on this farm he had a duck, E-I-E-I-O.
   With a quack-quack here and a quack-quack there,
   Here a quack, there a quack, everywhere a quack-quack,
   An oink-oink here, an oink-oink there,
   Here an oink, there an oink, everywhere an oink-oink,
   A moo-moo here, a moo-moo there,
   Here a moo, there a moo, everywhere a moo-moo,
   Old MacDonald had a farm, E-I-E-I-O.

*You can add more animals if you like.*

131

# A SEED IN THE GROUND

Words and Music by
Connie Kaldor

2. If you've got the sun,
   And if you've got the rain,
   Plant a little seed in the old back lane.
   You wish and you pray and you keep the weeds down,
   And you might find, oh you might find
   A shoot growing out from the root from the seed in the ground.

3. If you've got the sun,
   And if you've got the rain,
   Plant a little seed in the old back lane.
   You wish and you pray and you keep the weeds down,
   And you might find, oh you might find
   A stem growing out from the shoot from the root
       from the seed in the ground.

4. If you've got the sun,
   And if you've got the rain,
   Plant a little seed in the old back lane.
   You wish and you pray and you keep the weeds down,
   And you might find, oh you might find
   A blossom growing out from the stem from the shoot
       from the root from the seed in the ground.

5. If you've got the sun,
   And if you've got the rain,
   Plant a little seed in the old back lane.
   You wish and you pray and you keep the weeds down,
   And you might find, oh you might find
   A seed growing out from the blossom from the stem
       from the shoot from the root from the seed in the ground.

# The Three Little Pigs

*Another version of a familiar folk tale*

One sunny day long ago, three little pigs started out on the road to the brickyard. They wanted bricks so that each one could build a house of his very own. But the road was hot and dusty, and soon one little pig slowed to a stop.

"You go ahead," he said to his brothers. "I'm going to build a house right here with that bundle of straw in the field."

"But a house of straw is no good," said one little pig. "The first strong wind will blow it away!"

"He's right," said the other. "Don't be lazy. Come on!"

But the first little pig was stubborn. He stayed where he was, built a house out of straw, and was very happy until a big, hungry wolf knocked at his door. "Little pig, little pig," called the wolf. "Let me come in!"

"Not by the hair of my chinny chin chin!" said the pig.

"All right then," growled the wolf. "I'll huff and I'll puff and I'll blow your house in!" So he huffed and he puffed and made such a wind that the straw house fell to pieces and blew away. The little pig ran as fast as he could and was able to hide in a haystack.

Meanwhile, the second and third little pigs were still on the way to the brickyard when they saw a bundle of straight sticks lying in a ditch.

"That's for me!" shouted the second little pig. "Sticks instead of bricks! I'm going to build my house right here!"

"That's crazy," said the third little pig. "Sticks are not much better than straw. A really strong wind could blow your house to smithereens!"

The second little pig simply wouldn't listen, and he built his house of sticks right then and there. He had just settled in when the wolf came knocking at his door. "Little pig, little pig, let me come in," called the wolf.

"Not by the hair of my chinny chin chin," the pig replied.

"All right, you asked for it," snarled the wolf. "I'll huff and I'll puff and I'll blow your house in!" So he huffed and he puffed, and the little pig watched as the sticks began to bend and break. Then suddenly, his house collapsed in a heap. Luckily, as the wolf leapt hungrily towards the little pig, his foot caught on a stick and down he went, so the little pig had time to run and hide in a nearby haystack.

Meanwhile, the third little pig had reached the brickyard, bought a load of bricks, and built himself a sturdy brick house. He was busy in his kitchen making a pot of soup, when the same hungry wolf came knocking at the door. "Little pig, little pig, let me come in," he called.

"Not by the hair of my chinny chin chin!" replied the pig, who knew very well that the wolf was not at all interested in soup, but wanted a supper of fat little pig!

"All right, stand back!" snapped the wolf, "because I'll huff and I'll puff and I'll blow your house in!" So he huffed and he puffed and he huffed some more, but that brick house didn't fall or sway or even shake. It stood there firm and secure, with the third little pig safe inside.

The wolf was furious and hungrier than ever. Determined to get the little pig, he climbed to the roof and stepped into the chimney. "Aha!" he said to himself. "*Now* I'll have pig for supper!"

Down the chimney he slid, landing with a great splash in the big pot of soup cooking on the fire. The soup was so hot he zoomed right back up the chimney and was last seen scorching across the fields leaving a vapour trail behind him. The little pigs were safe, and the two who were hiding in the haystack came out and made their way to their brother's brick house. They knocked timidly on the door, and called out together, "You were right. We should have built our houses out of brick."

"Never mind," said their brother. "There's lots of room in this house for all three of us. Come on in and make yourself right at home."

That's what they did, and together in the fine, sturdy brick house, the three little pigs lived happily ever after.

### Tom, Tom, the Piper's Son

Tom, Tom, the piper's son,
Stole a pig, and away he run.
The pig was eat, and Tom was beat,
And Tom went roaring down the street.

Tom, Tom, the piper's son,
He learned to play when he was young,
But all the tune that he could play
Was "Over the hills and far away."

Now, Tom with his pipe made such a noise,
That he pleased both the girls and boys,
And they stopped to hear him play
"Over the hills and far away."

# THE FARMER IN THE DELL

Traditional

1. The far-mer in the dell, The far-mer in the dell,

Hi - ho the der - ry O, The far-mer in the dell.

2. The farmer takes the wife,
   The farmer takes the wife,
   Hi ho the derry O,
   The farmer takes the wife.

3. The wife takes the child,
   The wife takes the child,
   Hi ho the derry O,
   The wife takes the child.

4. The child takes the nurse,
   The child takes the nurse,
   Hi ho the derry O,
   The child takes the nurse.

5. The nurse takes the dog,
   The nurse takes the dog,
   Hi ho the derry O,
   The nurse takes the dog.

6. The dog takes the cat,
   The dog takes the cat,
   Hi ho the derry O,
   The dog takes the cat.

7. The cat takes the rat,
   The cat takes the rat,
   Hi ho the derry O,
   The cat takes the rat.

### Higgelty-Piggelty

Higgelty-Piggelty, my black hen,
She lays eggs for gentlemen,
Sometimes eight, or nine, or ten!
Higgelty-Piggelty, my black hen.

### The Cock

The cock crows in the morning
To tell us to rise,
And he that lies late
Will never be wise,
For early to bed
And early to rise
Is the way to be healthy
And wealthy and wise.

### Big Brown Cow

Mooooo!
I'm a big brown cow
And I like to munch
Clover and sweet grass
For breakfast and lunch.

The grass turns to milk,
To butter and cheese,
And then there's ice cream
As sweet as you please!
Mooooo!

# OATS, PEAS, BEANS, AND BARLEY GROW

Traditional

1. Oats, peas, beans, and bar - ley grow, Oats, peas, beans, and bar - ley grow, Do you or I or an - y - one know How oats, peas, beans, and bar - ley grow?

2. First the farmer plants the seeds,
   Stands up tall and takes his ease,
   He stamps his feet and claps his hands
   And turns around to view his lands.

3. Oats, peas, beans and barley grow,
   Oats, peas, beans and barley grow,
   Do you or I or anyone know
   How oats, peas, beans and barley grow?

**A Bee Sat on My Nose**

Now, what do you suppose?
A bee sat on my nose.   (*"Land" a finger on your nose.*)
Then what do you think?
He gave me a wink   (*Wink.*)
And said, "I beg your pardon,
I thought you were the garden."   (*Make flying away motions.*)

**139**

# DRY BONES

Traditional

Dem bones, dem bones, dem dry bones. Dem bones, dem bones, dem dry bones. Dem

bones, dem bones, dem dry bones. Now hear the word of the Lord. 1. Now the

toe bone con-nec-ted to the an-kle bone. The an-kle bone con-nec-ted to the shin bone. The

shin bone con-nec-ted to the knee bone. Now hear the word of the Lord. Dem

140

*Chorus:* Dem bones, dem bones, etc.

2. The knee bone connected to
   the thigh bone.
   The thigh bone connected to
   the hip bone.
   The hip bone connected to
   the back bone.
   Now hear the word of the Lord.
   *Chorus:* Dem bones, etc.

3. The back bone connected to
   the shoulder bone.
   The shoulder bone connected to
   the neck bone.
   The neck bone connected to
   the head bone.
   Now hear the word of the Lord.
   *Chorus:* Dem bones, etc.

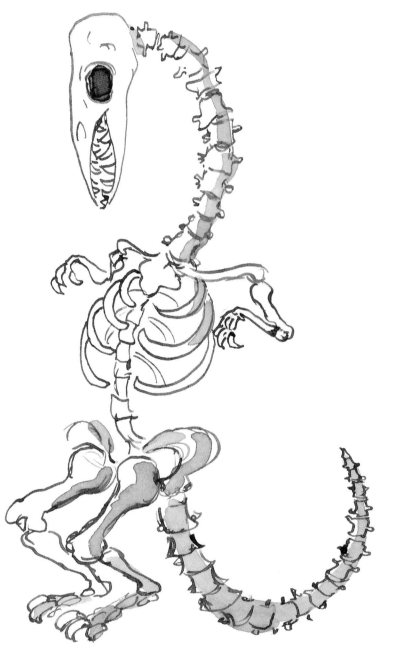

*The Wordbird knows the answer to this one.*
*Do you?*
Why didn't the skeleton go to the dance?

Because he had no body to go with!

**141**

# The Ballad of Slippery Sam

*by Pat Patterson*

I'm Slippery Samuel Smithers. That's me.
Come sit down a while, right here by my knee.
I'll tell you my tale (and I swear not to boast)
Of the fortune I buried, and why I'm a ghost.
    Derry down, down, down derry down.

When I was a young man, I travelled afar
To lands where the fiercest of headhunters are,
For many extravagant tales had been told
Of their diamonds and rubies and silver and gold.
    Derry down, down, down derry down.

I sneaked through the jungle as swift as a cat,
And there in a circle, the headhunters sat
A-counting their jewels and chortling with glee,
Not dreaming that they were observed, by me!
    Derry down, down, down derry down.

They counted them out, then they counted them back
Into something that looked like a big leather sack,
And when it was filled, I followed my plan;
I let out a whoop and I grabbed it and ran!
    Derry down, down, down derry down.

I zigged and I zagged as I fled through the dark.
The headhunters' arrows flew wide of their mark,
And even with spears they were simply no use
For they all had drunk far too much pineapple juice.
    Derry down, down, down derry down.

They lunged for my ankles, they snatched at my wrist,
They did flying tackles but all of them missed.
Each fellow who grabbed me would let out a gasp.
He couldn't believe that I slipped from his grasp.
    Derry down, down, down derry down.

My secret, at last, I am going to release;
I'd covered myself with a coating of grease
Obtained from a very fat roast leg of lamb.
And that's why I'm known as Slippery Sam.
    Derry down, down, down derry down.

I ran with my fortune and buried the lot
Some place in these woods, but where, I forgot,
And when I remembered, alas 'twas too late
For I'd died of old age at a hundred and eight.
    Derry down, down, down derry down.

Today I'm a ghost, so I'm pale and I'm gaunt,
The way one should look when attempting to haunt.
And as for my fortune, just keep well away
For Slippery Sam is on duty today!
    Derry down, down, down derry down.

# OVER THE RIVER

Traditional

Ov- er the riv-er and through the wood to grand-fa-ther's house we go; \_\_\_\_\_ The horse knows the way to car - ry the sleigh through white and drift - ed snow. \_\_\_\_\_

Ov- er the riv-er and through the wood, Oh how the wind does blow! \_\_\_\_\_ It

144

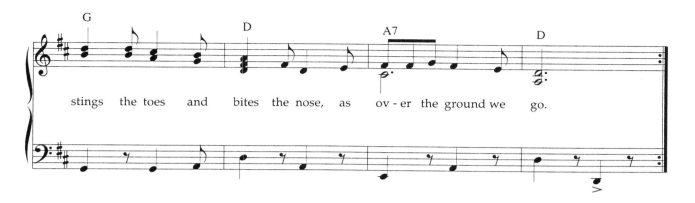

stings the toes and bites the nose, as ov-er the ground we go.

*All the actions that go with this
little finger play can be done while
you're sitting down. Try them as
you say the rhyme.*

## Finger Play

Little Arabella Miller
Found a woolly caterpillar.   *(Tickle your palm.)*
First it crawled up on her mother   *(Fingers crawl up one arm.)*
Then up on her little brother.   *(Fingers crawl up the other arm.)*
They said, "Arabella Miller!   *(Fingers of both hands tickle your face.)*
Put away that caterpillar!"   *(Put your hands behind your back.)*

Little Arabella Miller   *(Do the same things as before until...)*
Found a woolly caterpillar.
First it crawled up on her brother,
Then up on her dear grandmother.
Gran said, "Arabella Miller,   *(Gently stroke the back of your hand.)*
How I love your caterpillar."

Grandfather had some wheat and rye.
He put it out in the barn to dry.
Out came the mice to have some fun.
Up jumped the cat and made them all run.

145

# FATHER'S OLD GREY WHISKERS

Traditional

*Verse*

1. I have a dear old dad-dy, For whom I night-ly pray. He has a set of whisk-ers That are

*Chorus*

al - ways in the way. They're al - ways in the way, The cows eat them for hay. They

hide the dirt on dad - dy's shirt; They're al - ways in the way. (2. A - )

2. Around the supper table,
   We make a happy group,
   Until dear Father's whiskers
   Get tangled in the soup.
   *Chorus:* They're always, etc.

3. Father had a strong back,
   But now it's all caved in.
   He stepped upon his whiskers
   And walked up to his chin.
   *Chorus:* They're always, etc.

4. The birdies like my daddy,
   They think he is the best,
   They use his old grey whiskers
   To build themselves a nest.
   *Chorus:* They're always, etc.

5. The cat and dog both love him,
   He's father of the week,
   They run around his whiskers
   And play "Go hide and seek."
   *Chorus:* They're always, etc.

6. We have a dear old brother,
   He has a Ford machine.
   He uses Father's whiskers
   To strain the gasoline.
   *Chorus:* They're always, etc.

# HE'S MY BROTHER

Words and Music by
Connie Kaldor

148

both-ered by a bul-ly in the school-yard, And ev'-ry-bo-dy else is just stand-in' all a-round, I know they'll

*(Spoken: no tempo)*

jump in and bite that bu l-ly's leg, And kick and scratch and help me

*a tempo*

bring that bul - ly down. _____ 'Cause he's my

2. And if they're caught by old Darth Vader,
   Darth Vader sends them up to the middle of space,
   I know I'm gonna search all over this universe until I find them
   'Cause no one else could take their place.
   *Chorus:* 'Cause he's my brother, etc.

3. And if I'm cornered by a real fierce tiger
   With a great long tail, big teeth and red tongue,
   I know they'll grab that tiger by the tail and swing him round
   And swing that tiger to kingdom come.
   *Chorus:* 'Cause he's my brother, etc.

149

The Wordbird says there are lots of different words for saying goodbye. In English we say "So long!" "I'll be seeing you!" or "See you later!"

Other languages have other words. Here are some other ways to say goodbye.

Adieu *(French)*          Aloha *(Hawaiian)*

Adios *(Spanish)*         Auf wiedersehen *(German)*

Addio *(Italian)*          Dasvidániya *(Russian)*

Adeus *(Portuguese)*      Shalom *(Hebrew)*

Maybe you can add to this list. But whichever way you say it, remember what Fred always says and don't forget to look after each other. Goodbye!

# JIM ALONG JOSIE

**Chorus:** Hey jim along, jim along Josie,
Hey jim along, jim along Jo. *(Repeat.)*

3. Skip jim along, jim along Josie, etc.
   *Chorus:* Hey jim along, etc.

4. Run jim along, jim along Josie, etc.
   *Chorus:* Hey jim along, etc.

*You can sing "fly," "jump," "bounce" or
anything you like to make more verses.*

# YOU AND ME TIME

Words and Music by
Sandy Tobias Offenheim

you" time. _____ )   My ve - ry fav'- rite "spec-ial thing to do" time. _____ )   Time for hav-ing

FUN!   Time   for hav -ing FUN! _____ )   One   to   one. _____   Not

five,   not   four,   not   three, _____   just TWO. _____

Me and  you, _____   Me and  you, _____

Me and  you! _____

**153**

# WE'RE GONNA SHINE

Traditional

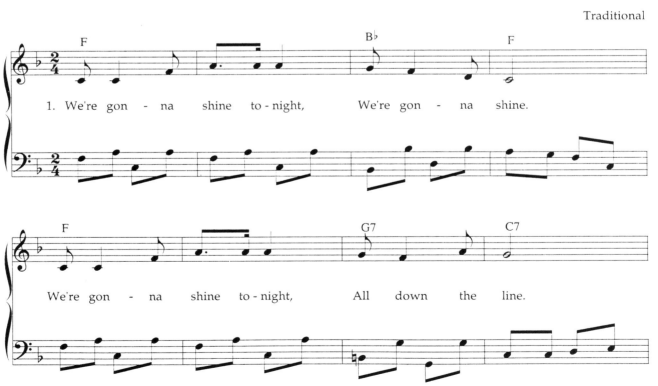

1. We're gon - na shine to - night, We're gon - na shine.

We're gon - na shine to - night, All down the line.

We're all dressed up to-night, We're feel - ing fine. When the sun goes down and the moon comes up, We're gon - na shine.

*Let's sing it in French!*

2. On va briller ce soir,
   On va briller.
   On va briller ce soir,
   On va chanter.
   Tout pomponné ce soir,
   On est très bien.
   Le soleil se couche
   Et la lune se lève,
   On va briller.

*This time, try it in Spanish.*

3. Vamos brillar esta noche,
   Vamos brillar.
   Vamos brillar esta noche
   Aquí por alla.
   Todos estan tan felices
   Quieren cantar.
   Cuando hay una luna
   En el cielo,
   Vamos brillar.

# Acknowledgments

Care has been taken to trace ownership of the copyright material in this book. Information will be welcome which will enable the publisher to rectify any reference or credit in subsequent editions.

Grateful acknowledgment is made to the following for permission to use copyright material: Joy Alexander for the music of "The Wordbird Song"; Mark Baldwin for the song "Walking"; Berandol Music Ltd. for the song "You and Me Time" by Sandy Offenheim; Branch Group Music Publishing for the song "I Am the Wind" and the adaptation of the song "The Cat Came Back" by Fred Penner; Coyote Entertainment Group, Inc. for the songs "He's My Brother," "If You Love a Hippopotamus" and "A Seed in the Ground" by Connie Kaldor; Bob King, Armchair Publishing, for the song "Friends"; Terry McManus for the song "I Like You"; Janis Nostbakken for the stories "Bubba's Bath," "Fat Cat," "Gail the Snail" and "Henny Penny"; Dodi Robb for part of the lyrics of "The Puddle Song."

Many of the stories in this book are traditional fables and folk tales which have been specially adapted for *Fred Penner's Place*.

By Pat Patterson: "The Lion and the Mouse," "The North Wind and the Sun," "The Grasshopper and the Ants," "The Tortoise and the Hare," "The Princess and the Pea," "Stone Soup," "Three Billy Goats Gruff," "The Three Little Pigs."

By Peg McKelvey: "The Three Wishes," "The Dog and the Bone," "The Talkative Turtle," "The Magic Spaghetti Pot," "The Rainbow in Lake Louise."

The piano arrangements were created by Jack Turner. They are easy to play, yet attractive and satisfying.

# The Editors

Pat Patterson is well known as a writer and broadcaster, working in documentary films, musical programs and radio documentaries, as well as films and programs for children.
Originating writer of TVO's *The Polka Dot Door*, she has collaborated with Dodi Robb on stage musicals, including the durable fantasies *The Dandy Lion* and *The Popcorn Man*. She is the author of *Hickory Dickory Duck* and has contributed many features to *Chickadee Magazine*.
Pat Patterson was initiating writer of *Fred Penner's Place* and continues to contribute scripts and lyrics. In 1986 she received the John Drainie Award for Distinguished Contribution to Broadcasting.

Peg McKelvey began her career in the editorial offices of a large publishing house where she was responsible for the production of many books, mostly for children. Later, she combined freelance editing with writing — educational films, musicals, books and television scripts — again, mostly for children. She was a member of the writing team for the award-winning CBC series *Mr. Dressup* from its beginning, and has been writing for *Fred Penner's Place* since 1986.


# The Illustrator

Marie Day likes to draw pictures and read — especially fairy tales and stories for children.
Well known for her theatrical design, where she has worked in everything from opera to *Anne of Green Gables*, she has just launched a new career as author and illustrator of books for young and old. Her book on fossil-hunter Mary Anning was published in the spring of 1992.

# Index

(Titles of songs in italics)

THE END